BRAIN
MATTERS

HOW TO HELP ANYONE LEARN
ANYTHING USING NEUROSCIENCE

MARGIE MEACHAM

Brain Matters: How to help anyone learn anything
Copyright © Margie Meacham

Dedication

This book is dedicated to the love of my life, my husband, David. He inspires me, believes in me, and makes all my neurons fire with excitement.

Acknowledgements

Some of the material in this book first appeared online in the Science of Learning Community of Practice on the Association for the Talent Development (ATD) website. These articles are used with the permission of ATD. I am a proud member of this outstanding organization and I recommend it to anyone who is passionate about learning. Visit atd.org for more information.

TABLE OF CONTENTS

Brain Matters: How to help anyone learn anything using neuroscience

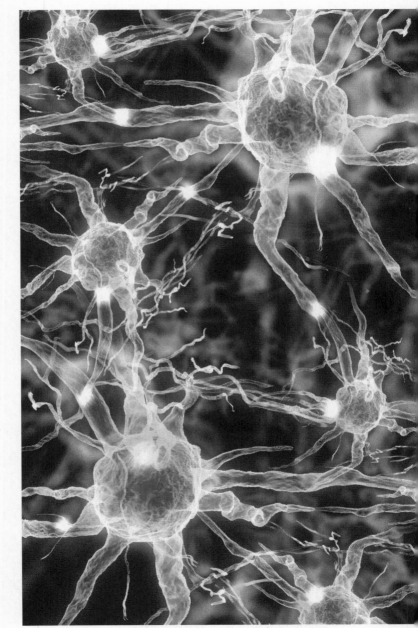

INTRODUCTION

I magine sitting next to Marie Curie in her lab as she discovers the power of radioactivity or walking with Neil Armstrong on the moon. Maybe you are seeing the DNA double-helix for the first time with Watson, Crick, and Wilson, or looking through a telescope with Galileo to see the moons of Jupiter. If you had the chance to be a part of these great moments of discovery, would you take it?

If you said "yes," then you're in luck. The human race is embarking on a great adventure. We are discovering how the brain works by watching it in the very act of cognition. The brain, a quivering bundle of more than 400 billion neurons, uses electrical charges to transmit and store sensations, feelings, decisions, fears, thoughts, and even our sense of self, on a constant and ever-changing basis. Neuroscientists are starting to unlock the code that allows the sights, smells, and sounds of your seventh birthday to come alive in your memory as vividly as the first time you experienced them. Learning professionals are just starting to figure out what this wonderful, beautiful landscape of neurons, dendrites, and axons means to those of us who want to help people learn. If you are a teacher, a trainer, a leader or a parent, you are already on this journey, whether or not you have previously realized this fact.

In this book I take a look at some of the discoveries flowing from the field of neuroscience and apply them to our work as learning professionals. We'll talk about how your thoughts physically change your brain and how you can control your thoughts to manage your mood, intelligence, and overall health. We'll look at how the stress of change influences our brains to do strange and sometimes quite counter-productive things and we'll identify ways to help people deal with change by understanding and controlling their own responses to change. We'll explore the power of images, our brain's first language. And we'll talk about the different effects that verbs and nouns have on our actions.

Through all of this exploration, we'll look at how we can put this exciting new information into practical action. You'll no doubt discover that some of the things you've been doing to help people learn have now been empirically proven in a lab, with the full force of hard science. No doubt you'll also discover a thing or two you thought were true have turned out to be false in light of new information. That's how science works. Fifty years from now, I'm quite certain that some of the things that I share with you here will have been proven to be false, or at least incomplete, based on the knowledge that will be available in 2065. Who knows? You and I may still be around by then. Or, at the very least, we may have downloaded our consciousness onto a computer chip, so we can reread this book and update it together.

While I can't see that far into the future, I can guarantee that there have been new advances on every topic addressed in the book just since it was printed, so I urge you to visit the website listed at the end of this book for more information on our growing understanding of the application of neuroscience to learning.

This book is meant to be a series of brief conversations about how the brain works and how we can use that information to help people learn. You won't need to take a course in neuroscience to understand this book but you do need a basic map to help you navigate this exciting new world. Our first chapter, Neural Nuts and Bolts, will give you that map.

From there, the book is organized into general chapters, with several shorter essays relating to each chapter topic. You can read this book straight through, or jump around and read what interests you. Your brain will actually lead you to relevant content as you skim through the pages. In fact, if you pause for a moment, you may be able to feel the sensation of learning – that "aha" moment when you feel a "flash" of insight. It turns out that this is a very appropriate term for learning something new. Your brain is constantly sending electrical signals between cells. When you form a new idea or learn a new concept new physical connections form between cells and a flash of electro-chemical energy leaps from one cell to another. Our brains are literally "lighting up" as we learn and picturing that process as you read the book may actually speed up and heighten the learning effect.

I'd like to say "let's get started," but the truth is that you have already begun to form new neural connections, so let's continue with Chapter One, Neural Nuts and Bolts.

NEURAL NUTS AND BOLTS

Neuroscience and the Learning Professional

Through the use of brain imaging technology, scientists are able to observe a live subject in the process of making decisions, learning new skills, or retrieving memories. As learning professionals, we can apply these emerging insights to our work. In this space, I'm going to share some of this research and applications to the learning profession. Here are a few to get you started.

The brain is constantly learning

A common misconception prior to the development of brain imaging technology was that the adult brain was frozen at around the age of 18. The discovery of neuroplasticity revealed that the brain continues to remake itself every day, forming new neural pathways, pruning out unused pathways, and rerouting existing pathways in response to new experiences and stimuli. We do not choose this behavior; it is as natural and automatic as breathing.

What does this mean to you? We must always be aware of the entire learning experience. Our learners may be forming a different memory than the one we intend. For example, a boring presentation on customer service may actually be "teaching" participants that engaging with customers is boring!

The brain is a survival machine

Our brains have evolved over time through the process of Natural Selection. Individuals who were better at certain skills gained a competitive advantage and survived to pass their genes on to their offspring.

The survival imperative is key to understanding brain function today because even though we face fewer daily threats to our physical survival in normal daily life today, our brains are still hard-wired to protect us and keep us alive. This survival mechanism explains the way we respond to change and stress.

The brain interprets these stimuli as threats to life and triggers all kinds of behaviors that might not be productive in corporate life, but were extremely valuable in keeping our ancestors alive in different times. We'll talk more about these survival mechanisms in future articles.

The brain is distributed throughout body

Some writers speak of the mind-body connection to explain how our physical well-being affects our ability to think and learn. However, the reality is far deeper than a mere connection. The brain is made up of about 100 billion neurons, or brain cells. These neurons are connected to all the other neurons in the nervous system, which tells the brain what is happening inside and outside of our bodies.

A neuron in your hand fires a pain signal to the brain when you prick your finger; that neuron is an extension of the brain, which responds by pulling away from the source. When you think of the brain as being distributed throughout your body, you can see how the conditions of the training room or the ergonomics of the elearning environment will affect the overall learning experience. You may be generating unintended consequences through the design of your e-learning interface or the arrangement of your classroom.

Moving forward

The science of learning is an exciting new frontier for our profession. Over the next few years, we can expect many changes in how we approach our work, as we find more ways to apply the science of learning to our talent development efforts.

References

• Types of Brain Imaging Techniques, Michael DeMitri, M.D.
http://psychcentral.com/lib/types-of-brain-imaging-techniques/0001057
• What is Brain Plasticity? Kendra Cherry.
http://psychology.about.com/od/biopsychology/f/brain-plasticity.htm
• Enhancing the plasticity of the brain: Max Cynader at TEDxStanleyPark
https://www.youtube.com/watch?v=Chr3rQ6Vpcw
• Understanding Evolution: Natural Selection
http://evolution.berkeley.edu/evolibrary/article/evo_25
• Brain Rules, John Medina
http://www.brainrules.net/survival
• Mind-Body Connection, Natural Health Perspective
http://naturalhealthperspective.com/resilience/mind-body-connection.html
• How Many Neurons are there in the Brain? Kendra Cherry
http://psychology.about.com/od/biopsychology/f/how-many-neurons-in-the-brain.htm
• Neuroscience for Kids, University of Washington
https://faculty.washington.edu/chudler/cells.html

Left-Brained/Right Brained
and Other Falsehoods

True or false: Left-brain dominance is marked by a preference for logic and analysis.

In Chapter One, I suggested that you might find some of your previously held "truths" proven false by the latest research in brain science. Here is one of those "truths" that I personally thought was fully vetted and took as fact: there are specific left- and right-brain preferences in cognition styles.

The theory

The theory goes something like this: We know that the brain is separated into two hemispheres and the brain tends to localize some activities in one hemisphere or the other. The corpus callosum is a massive, high-speed, Internet-like connection for the brain, allowing the two halves to communicate back and forth. Working with epilepsy patients for whom this connection was severed, Dr. Roger W. Sperry concluded that:

- different types of thinking occur in different hemispheres
- the left hemisphere is dedicated to logic and analysis
- the right hemisphere is dedicated to intuition and creativity
- people are not entirely left- or right-brained, but we do have a preference for one type of thinking over another

Sperry won a Nobel Prize for his work on the "split brain" in 1981. (Ironically, Dr. Sperry was awarded a "split prize" with David H. Hubel and Torsten N. Wiesel.) His particular treatment is still used to control severe cases of epilepsy, and it is true that people who have had this surgery demonstrate significant differences in how they process information and sensory input.

The industry

As this discovery started gaining popular momentum, an entire cottage industry around left-brain/right-brain thinking emerged. Today you can take a test to discover which side is dominant for you, learn how to recognize left or right dominance in others, perform exercises to develop the other side of your brain, and so on. The only trouble is, the underlying principle behind all these products and services may be completely false.

The truth

As far back as 2004, researchers at the U.S. Army Research Institute for the Behavioral and Social Sciences discovered that mathematically "gifted" boys demonstrated a powerful collaboration between the two hemispheres when performing complex mathematical problems. They concluded that the brains of these boys must be significantly different than the average brain and suggested that perhaps these "math-genius brains" were more adept and signaling back and forth across the corpus callosum.

But a group of neuroscientists at the University of Utah have come upon a different explanation for the 2004 results. Working over a two-year period, they scanned the brains of 1,011 people between the ages of seven and 29. After looking at 7,000 regions in each individual brain, they could find absolutely no evidence that there is a preference for left or right brained activity for any individual in the study. So it isn't just the spectacularly gifted who have this characteristic—it's all of us.

Just to be clear, this research is not debunking the proven fact of lateralization of brain function. We know that some functions take place on one side of the brain, and others take place in another. What has now been disproven is the theory that we each have a tendency to **prefer** one side of our brain over another.

What does this mean for human capital professionals?

If you are using tests for brain preference in your hiring or employee development process, you might want to stop—at least until more data is in. You also might need to review the language in some of your training materials to ensure that you aren't making broad statements about left- and right-brained people.

More importantly, we should all take some time to consider what this new discovery tells us about how we think. The two halves of our brains are in a state of constant collaboration, and they seem to be equally important to the process of thinking. How might this newly discovered **preference for balance** translate into practice?

- Should we look at how we structure the workplace itself, and determine if the physical environment is overly preferential to one side of our brain over another?
- Should we teach people to understand how their brain talks to itself to solve complex problems?
- Do we start training managers to look for left/right balance in their hiring efforts?

I don't have the answers to these and other questions that this astounding study poses. But I do know one thing: Somebody needs to update Wikipedia.

References

• Dan Izzo, The Corpus Callosum,
https://www.youtube.com/watch?v=7zOa3LLrHKc
• Roger Wolcott Sperry, Wikipedia,
http://en.wikipedia.org/wiki/Roger_Wolcott_Sperry
• Nobelprize.org, The Nobel Prize in Physiology or Medicine 1981,
http://www.nobelprize.org/nobel_prizes/medicine/laureates/1981
• Ctshad, Severed Corpus Callosum,
https://www.youtube.com/watch?v=IfGwsAdS9Dc

• Kathleen Lees, Are You 'Right-Brained' or 'Left-Brained'? Myth Debunked, http://www.scienceworldreport.com/articles/8901/20130819/right-brained-left-myth-debunked.htm
• Wikipedia, Lateralization of brain function, http://en.wikipedia.org/wiki/Lateralization_of_brain_function#Lateralized_cognitive_processes
• Lou Adler, Use the Two-question Whole-Brain Interview to Assess Everything, http://www.ere.net/2011/02/18/use-the-two-question-whole-brain-interview-to-assess-everything/

Neural Nuts and Bolts

The Expectation Effect

David Epstein studies the changes in athletic achievements and how these achievements related to changes in technology, genetics, and human beliefs about the limits of the human body. What he has discovered is that our brains have a built-in "limiter"—an area in the brain that keeps us from hurting ourselves by pushing our bodies too close to our breaking point.

But recent advances in "extreme" sports have found ways to bypass the limiter, opening up a wider definition of what is possible for the human body. Athletes have begun tapping into this concept to override the brain, so that they can train harder and get faster, more dramatic results.

As human capital professionals, we can help people overcome different types of limiters that might be holding them back from peak performance on the job. But first, we need to understand where the limits come from: the Expectation Effect.

Great expectations

In George Bernard Shaw's play Pygmalian, a professor teaches a London flower girl how to speak and act like a duchess. Because he presents her as such to the members of high society, they see her as one of them. They see what they expect. In one study testing the Expectation Effect, teachers were told that a group of students with average abilities was "gifted." These students performed better in academic tests after a few months—because the teachers were spending more time with them and giving them more challenging assignments.

Managers can fall into the same trap, buying into an employee's reputation for high potential and treating them accordingly. The scary thing about the Expectation Effect is that it is working double-duty. It affects the perceptions of people who are evaluating the individual's performance, and it also influences the people being evaluated. Someone who is being treated as exceptional begins to see themselves as such, which leads to even more increased performance.

Sadly, the Expectation Effect is equally effective at producing poor performance.

Real-life example

Consider a case study of a two little girls in first grade. She is slower at learning to read than most of her classmates, often misspells even simple words, can't solve simple math problems, and her handwriting is backwards and almost illegible. Her teachers label her as "slow" and put her in "special needs" classes.

In these classes, she doesn't really get much help learning how to read, but she does very quickly come to understand that she isn't very smart. As the girl grows older, her parents and teachers steer her to vocational courses and discourage any thought of attending college. She agrees. After all, college is for smart people. She ends up in a minimum-wage job, which is just what everyone has expected for her.

Another child exhibits the same early symptoms. Her first-grade teacher recognizes that the child is dyslexic and meets with her parents to put together some learning strategies to help her catch up with her classmates. Her family and her teachers emphasize her gifts, and encourage her to succeed. She grows up being keenly aware of how her brain works, learning to leverage her strengths and compensate for weaknesses. By high school, she's the class valedictorian. She goes on to a successful career with an advanced degree and considers herself capable of just about anything.

That second child was me. I am so grateful to my father, who told me "you are not stupid," and insisted that I can do anything I set my mind to. I soon discovered that he was right.

Sadly, there are too many versions of the first child's story. You may have experienced some version of it yourself. You may have been told you weren't good at math, weren't athletic, didn't have any common sense, or any number of other failings that your brain then found a way to validate. Breaking out of these self-imposed limiters can be difficult—but not impossible.

Breaking limits

Shakespeare's Hamlet tells us, "There is nothing either good or bad, but thinking makes it so."

Norman Vincent Peale wrote The Power of Positive Thinking more than 60 years ago, yet the exact mechanisms that produce these results are still a mystery to us. That hasn't stopped a whole cottage industry from growing up around training your brain and finding your hidden talents. While these programs may have some value, the clinical proof has yet to be seen.

And still I believe in the power of our endless curiosity as a species. I believe that we will harness at least some of the brain's power to transform human performance in my lifetime. I believe it because I believe that I've already personally experienced it. And of course, because this is what I'm expecting, there is a very good chance that I'll find it.

References

• David Epstein, Are athletes really getting faster, better, stronger? http://www.ted.com/talks/david_epstein_are_athletes_really_getting_faster_better_stronger

• Sharon Begley, Expectations May Alter Outcomes Far More Than We Realize, http://www.charleswarner.us/articles/WSJExpectations.htm

• Norman Vincent Peale, The Power of Positive Thinking

NEUROSCIENCE
AND THE
ORGANIZATION

Your Brain in (Work) Space

At the University of Waterloo in Canada, scientists are studying how we humans interact with our man-made environments and what effects these interactions have on our brains. They're trying to figure out why some spaces attract us, and other spaces don't. The insights from Waterloo and other studies could one day inform the way we build our cities, our schools, and our workspaces, but the idea is hardly new.

William Whyte, a pioneer in urban planning, conducted an exhaustive study of the public spaces of New York City in 1969. In his book The Social Life of Small Urban Spaces, Whyte shared his discoveries, including the insight that people tend to gather in smaller, more intimate spaces. Whyte's influence can be seen in the sub-structure of New York's Central Park, the downtown areas of San Antonio and other cities, and workspaces such as Google, Steelcase and others. What makes Whyte's accomplishments all the more remarkable is that he had no access to neuroscience data to lead him to his conclusions. He relied on disciplined fact-gathering and relentless observation to tell him how people in large groups interact with their environments. Now, thanks to neuroscience, we also know why.

Measuring brain waves to understand our reaction to space

In the Waterloo study, scientists built several different types of urban spaces, from extremely orderly to what they describe as "chaotic," and then measured their subjects' brain responses as they explored the spaces. Here is what they discovered:

Logical, orderly layouts were far less engaging than other models.

People tended to spend less time in these models, and their brains showed lower levels of arousal and excitement. In contrast, when the underlying structure of the space wasn't readily apparent, subjects responded with greater interest and put more effort into exploring the space. Their brains indicated a higher level of overall engagement and attention.

The ability to see a green space affects subjects emotionally and physically.

Subjects who had a view of an area with green plants reported happier moods than subjects without this view, and their brains showed higher levels of relaxation.

Building the brain-friendly workplaces

We are starting to see the application of brain science to the design of office buildings and workspaces. The Academy of Neuroscience for Architecture professes to be "the only organization in the world devoted to the goal of building intellectual bridges between neuroscience and architecture."

Their goal is to re-educate the architectural profession, but the organization's site is certainly worth a visit for anyone involved in human capital management.

If those materials provide a little bit more information than you're looking for, try this slide show of tips to build offices that foster creativity.

What does the future hold?

I'm convinced that we will continue to find more ways to apply our understanding of the brain to the way we manage our world, and I'm certainly not alone in that opinion. In 2010, *U.S. News &World Report* envisioned future workspaces with more gathering spaces, fewer cubes, on-site lounges, standing meetings, and other ideas that have their roots in discoveries from neuroscience. Where we end up is up to us—and our incredible brains.

References

•William Whyte, The Social Life of Small Urban Spaces, http://www.pps.org/product/the-social-life-of-small-urban-spaces/
•Academy of Neuroscience for Architecture: http://www.anfarch.org/
•Inc., 10 Office Design Tips to Foster Creativity, http://www.inc.com/ss/jessica-stillman/10-office-design-tips-foster-creativity?slide=0
•Rick Newman, The Office of the Future, http://money.usnews.com/money/business-economy/slideshows/the-office-of-the-future/1

The Neuroscience of Goals

If you are one of the many people who make resolutions at the start of a new year, you may have found that you start with great intentions but fall short of your goal over and over again. Don't feel too badly. After one month, only about 64 percent of resolutions are still in force and by six months that number drops to less than 50 percent.

The same thing happens when leaders try to set goals for their employees. Let's look at the performance improvement process through the lens of New Year's resolutions and see what neuroscience can teach us to make both more successful.

The Brain on Change

So why is change so hard? One of the key points in that article is that our brain is structured with one primary purpose: to keep us alive so that we can transmit our genes to the next generation. *The Selfish Gene* by Richard Dawkins, is a classic work on the subject.

Historically, change has often been dangerous. So we have become hard-wired to avoid and resist it at every turn. And yet, when faced with a change that has the potential to make us more likely to survive, some brains are able to adapt more easily than others. It turns out that health and lifestyle choices have a significant effect on the brain's ability to change.

Changing the Brain to Change Behavior

Daniel Amen has studied over 63,000 brains using brain imaging to study blood flow and activity patterns. He studies the connection between brain health and success in life and overall happiness. One interesting conclusion of his studies is that a healthy brain is much better equipped to make positive changes and stick to them. Want to lose weight, make more money, or spend more time with your family? The answer is the same: start by ensuring that your brain is healthy.

Rich Brain/Poor Brain

While taking up only 2 percent of our average body weight, the brain consumes more than 20 percent of the body's energy. This energy is transmitted through the blood, along with everything else we eat, drink, breathe or are exposed to in our environment. In her book, Starting Strong: A Mentoring Fable, Lois Zachary and Lory Fischler tells the story of a mentor and mentee. Along the way, the mentor learns that she must address the whole person if she is going to help her client achieve lasting changes in performance and behavior. Some of the brain health issues that she eventually addresses with her mentee include:

- examining preconceptions and negative thoughts
- maintaining healthy activity levels and diet
- making learning new things a daily habit
- unlearning (also called pruning) unproductive thoughts or conceptions

We can't eliminate change from our lives, but we can make it less painful by understanding the science behind our reactions to it.

References

•Statistic Brain, New Year's Resolution Statistics, http://www.statisticbrain.com/new-years-resolution-statistics/
•Richard Dawkins, The Selfish Gene
•Daniel Amen, Change your Life, Change your Brain
•University World News, The brain – Our most energy-consuming organ, http://www.universityworldnews.com/article.php?story=20130509171737492
•Lois Zachary and Lory Fischler, Starting Strong: A Mentoring Fable

Neuroscience and the Organization

Ethics and Neuroscience

Every time we experience an explosion of technological capabilities, we humans are faced with new choices to make. For example, when the first successful heart transplants were performed in the late 1960s, questions about ethical considerations arose: "How will we decide who gets a heart and who doesn't?" "Is it right to put a heart from a white person into a black person, or vice versa?" (Yes, folks were actually concerned about this at the time.)

Recently, a new test that appears to accurately predict your likelihood of developing Alzheimer's disease was developed. While further study is needed, there is the distinct possibility that in the very near future, you may able to take this test to find out if you are among the almost 5 million people who will contract this deadly brain disease.

Today, I want to explore the ethical questions that this and other advancements of neuroscience are posing.

Would You Want to Know?

If you could take the Alzheimer's test today, which is expected to be 90 percent accurate, *would you want to*? The answer is a very personal one, and I'm sure there are people on both sides. Let's assume that we agree that you have the right to know about any future illness you're likely to contract. But if you have the right to know, does anyone else? Would your spouse, parents, or children also have the right to know that they are very likely facing a major financial obligation to care for you in the future?

Should Your Employer Know About Your Individual Health Risks?

Part of the discussion about the new national healthcare program in the United States hinges around how companies can reduce costs associated with employee healthcare. Some would argue that being able to determine the risk factors of an employee, such as an individual's potential to develop an addiction, demonstrate violent behavior, or develop a serious disease is important data to help the company manage costs. Others argue that letting employers have this information would be a serious violation of privacy and individual rights.

Where Do You Stand?

Where do you stand on the ethical questions raised by the discoveries of neuroscience? As a human capital manager, you may find yourself making decisions about how to use what you know about your employee's brains in the not-so-different future.

References

• Ethical Issues in Neuroscience, Thomas Fuchs, 2006
• Empowering Brain Science with Neuroethics, Judy Illes, 2013
• Ethical Issues in Taking Neuroscience Research from Bench to Bedside, Alan Leschner, 2004

Neuroscience and the Organization

Leadership Starts
in the Brain

Most people would agree that today's leaders need to be experts at developing and building trust with their team members. This requirement has become even more important as Millennials have entered the workforce. So far, this generation seems to place a high value on collaboration and social connectedness in the workplace. These workers need to feel connected to their leaders and want to know that they have a relationship built on trust. There are thousands of books on leadership out there already, so what can neuroscience tell us about the process of building trust?

Oxytocin: the neurotransmitter of trust

A study in 2008 identified a neurochemical, called oxytocin, which makes the brain more receptive to feel trust towards a stranger. This same chemical is released in large amounts during sex and child birth, and is thought to trigger feelings of orgasm and mother-child bonding. Another study identified two distinct areas in the brain: One is activated when we are experiencing feelings of trust, and another is activated when we do not trust someone.

At the risk of sounding "politically incorrect," it makes perfect sense to me that the emotions of trust, orgasm, and maternal bonding all would be triggered by the same mechanism within our brains. There is a significant similarity in what is happening in each of these cases from an interpersonal point of view. A new relationship is being formed, and that means that trust must be established between the two parties.

Building trust as a leader

Our brains make a determination of the trustworthiness of a person within milliseconds of meeting him. This initial evaluation continues to be updated as more information is obtained and processed. The brain simultaneously is evaluating physical appearance, gestures, voice tone, the content of spoken communication, and many other factors. All of this is happening so quickly that most people will find it difficult to express exactly why they trust or distrust a person.

So how does a leader build trust? Here are a few suggestions based on how our brains process information:

- **Make people feel safe.** Our brains place top priority on survival, so any person who demonstrates that she can reduce or eliminate threats to others' survival is deemed trustworthy. Remember that in today's world, threats could mean a challenge to our physical survival, but also could mean a danger to our prestige, income, or comfort.
- **Demonstrate fairness.** Another study determined that people who played a computer game that was set up to place them at a disadvantage against other fictional players triggered the distrust portion of the brain, and also elicited feelings of anger and frustration.
- **Think about how you appear to others.** When we watch someone else, our brains are activated in the same way that the brain of the person we are observing is activated— through the function of special "mirror neurons." This means that you might unintentionally transfer your own feelings of distrust to others. The trick is that you can't fake trust; our brains can tell the difference. You actually must believe that your co-workers are trustworthy to transmit this signal to them. In turn, their brains will start feeling trust towards you as a result.

By understanding how the brain determines trustworthiness, we can help leaders to gain the trust of their team members. Neuroscience teaches us what great leaders always have known intuitively: *It starts by focusing on the needs of the team member, not your own. You can't fake it. You truly have to be trustworthy to be trusted.*

References

• Lauren, What is a Millennial? http://themilleniallegacy.com/the-millennial-generation/team-oriented/

• Paul J. Zak, The Neurobiology of Trust, http://www.scientificamerican.com/article/the-neurobiology-of-trust/

• Angelika Dimoka, What Does the Brain Tell Us About Trust and Distrust? Evidence from a Functional Neuroimaging Study, http://misq.org/what-does-the-brain-tell-us-about-trust-and-distrust-evidence-from-a-functional-neuroimaging-study.html

The Adolescent Brain
in the Workplace

Lately I've been catching myself saying things that make me sound like an old woman: "She looks way too young to be tending bar." "He's so immature. Were we like that at his age?" "When are these kids going to grow up and leave the house?"

I recently was heartened to learn that I'm not just growing older (although that's true). I'm also noticing a trend in human development that can be at least partially understood by neuroscience. It seems that adolescence—that period before we become adults—is growing longer.

In his book The Age of Opportunity, Laurence Steinberg makes the case that human beings are entering and staying in adolescence longer than ever before. This special phase in human development is starting earlier and lasting longer. If you think that you have only adult education to consider in your work; think again.

Many of the young people in the workplace and the vast majority of those in college are still in the adolescent phase of their development. Understanding how their brains work will give you a fighting chance to design meaningful learning experiences for this audience.

What Is Adolescence?

Steinberg defines adolescence as "the stage of development that begins with puberty and ends with economic and social independence." Based on his research, it is beginning as early as 10 and continues well into a person's 20s, which goes a long way to explain why your new recruits are working at the office and going home to their parents' house at the end of the day.

While the lengthening of adolescence has its roots in a combination of social-economic changes, it is much more than a societal trend. The brains of adolescents are significantly different than the brains of children or adults and must be understood and managed accordingly.

Characteristics of the Adolescent Brain

The most astonishing and powerful development of the human brain is its cerebral cortex. This outer shell of brain tissue is present in all primate and mammals, but the human brain has a much more developed cortex, giving us higher abilities to think, solve problems, learn, remember, and be self-aware.

In human evolution, we developed a way of folding this brain tissue over itself, giving us a lot more real estate—and a lot more neural networks to use to become human. In adolescents, this part of the brain is still developing, resulting in all kinds of behavioral issues, including:

- difficulty concentrating and remembering even routine tasks
- amped-up sexual drive
- willingness to take risks
- poor impulse control
- susceptibility to peer pressure
- heightened emotional responses and mood swings
- difficulty sleeping, which interferes with brain development

On the plus side, the brain at this stage in its development is exceptionally plastic. It is changing at a breathtakingly rapid rate compared to the adult brain, which continues to change, but at a slower pace. The brain is doing exactly what it should do for people between the ages of 10 and 25: it is preparing to be the brain of a successful adult but it isn't there yet.

What Can You Do?

As educators and leaders of people in the later stages of adolescence, we have an opportunity and a responsibility to help our young people make the most of this critical developmental stage. You will not be successful treating these people as fully formed adults. Rather, you must meet them where they are in the developmental continuum in order to be effective. Here are a few ideas suggested by recent findings:

Encourage physical activity, especially organized sports. These activities teach the brain to make quick decisions and create neural pathways related to team work, collaboration, motivation, and other critical life and workplace skills.

Channel risk-taking bias into exploration and experimentation. One of the last parts of the brain to fully develop is the part that helps us evaluate and mitigate risk. Research indicates that adolescents are more comfortable with risks presented by new situations. So why not make use of this brain characteristic for think tanks, product development, and brain storming?

Teach emotional control. Adolescents tend to process most experiences through the amygdala, a structure in the brain that is related to strong emotions and the triggering of the "flight or fight" response. This is why a traumatic event during this stage in life has a more lasting effect than if it were to occur later in life. You can help the young people in your organization develop a greater understanding and control of their own emotions, reducing conflict and drama in the workplace.

Encourage socializing with peers. The adolescent brain responds very positively to interactions with people of similar age and even tends to seek out social experiences. This is a valuable trait when one is at the age where finding a mate is a critical step to the survival of the species. It can also be a critical step towards building a network of future leaders in your organization. Make it easier for your young people to form connections with each other by creating reasons for them to socialize during and outside of work.

Limit exposure to alcohol. When compared to adult subjects, the adolescent brain reacts differently to alcohol, as a result of having a different chemistry than that of an adult. This adolescent brain chemistry results in higher tolerance for the sedative effect of alcohol, making it possible for the younger person to drink more before becoming sleepy or passing out. Alcohol also seems to have a greater adverse effect on several key brain functions in adolescents, including forming new memories and spatial awareness. These effects continue over the life of the subject, so that damage incurred at a young age continues into adulthood.

Provide plenty of just-in-time performance support. Because the adolescent brain is still learning how to learn, people in this stage of development often have trouble remembering routine tasks. Job aids such as checklists, process guides and graphic organizers are even more critical to support performance within this group.

Moving Forward

Child labor may be a thing of the past in most advanced societies, but adolescents are certainly in the workplace—and they are likely to continue to come to us in greater and greater numbers. We must be ready to apply the appropriate learning interactions to help these members of our team succeed.

And what about the other side of the spectrum: aging workers? What can our organizations do for the growing number of aging workers (like me) who are staying at work longer? Do their brains need targeted strategies as well? The answer is "yes," but we'll have to wait for another time to tackle that question.

References

• Laurence Steinberg, The Age of Opportunity
• National Institute of Health, The Teenage Brain: Still Under Construction, http://www.nimh.nih.gov/health/publications/the-teen-brain-still-under-construction/index.shtml
• Wikipedia, The Cerebral cortex, http://en.wikipedia.org/wiki/Cerebral_cortex
• Sarah Spinks, Adolescent Brains are Works in Progress, http://www.pbs.org/wgbh/pages/frontline/shows/teenbrain/work/adolescent.html
• Carl Zimmer: Why Athletes are Geniuses, http://discovermagazine.com/2010/apr/16-the-brain-athletes-are-geniuses
• Maia Szalavitz, Why the Teen Brain is Drawn to Risk, http://healthland.time.com/2012/10/02/why-the-teen-brain-is-drawn-to-risk/
• Sarah Spinks, One Reason Why Teens Respond Differently to the World; Immature Brain Circuitry, http://www.pbs.org/wgbh/pages/frontline/shows/teenbrain/work/onereason.html
• Maia Szalavitz, The Half-Baked Teen Brain: A Hazard or a Virtue? http://healthland.time.com/2011/09/16/the-half-baked-teen-brain-a-hazard-or-a-virtue/
• Susanne Hiller-Sturmhöfel, Ph.D., and H. Scott Swartzwelder, Ph.D., Alcohol's Effects on the Adolescent Brain—What Can Be Learned From Animal Models, http://pubs.niaaa.nih.gov/publications/arh284/213-221.htm
• Nicole Avery, Parenting Tips For Teenagers Vol 7 – The Teenage Brain, http://planningwithkids.com/2013/09/12/parenting-tips-for-teenagers-vol-7-the-teenage-brain/

Gamification and Engagement

In a recent study conducted by the Society of Human Resource Management (SHRM), employee engagement was identified as the "most important challenge facing HR organizations." Some interesting applications of neuroscience to the study of engagement have yielded promising results, by tapping into the brain's reward response system.

But reward programs can be expensive, leading many budget-strapped human capital managers to seek other options. In fact, there is evidence that monetary rewards, in absence of other cues that put that reward in context, may not even be the most effective option for stimulating and sustaining employee engagement.

Defining employee engagement

What does employee engagement look like? There are a variety of definitions out there, but here's one from *Forbes* magazine: "Employee engagement is the emotional commitment the employee has to the organization and its goals."

This definition, of course, is a long-accepted view of engagement based on outward, observable behavior. Until recently, we had no way of knowing what the employee was actually thinking or feeling, so we relied on visible behavior to gives us clues to their inner life.

Through brain imaging experiments on live subjects, we now know what a highly engaged brain looks like. Wouldn't we want all of your employees to have this sort of brain signature? Imagine the productivity gains that might be possible with a workforce full of highly engaged people.

We actually don't have to imagine those gains; the research tells us what companies with engaged employees are more productive than those with only average engagement.

So what can leaders do to engage their subjects to such a high degree? Should they offer rewards for performance, create successive levels of ever-increasing challenge and reward, build social communities of practice, or give top performers public recognition in front of their peers? All of the above and more have been well documented in books on leadership and motivation. But there is a new approach that may reveal even more promise: gamification of work.

Game play as the ultimate engagement lever

The key to understanding the power of video games is brain plasticity. The brain is constantly rebuilding and re-configuring itself, in response to every single experience. According to scientist Daphne Bavelier, frequent players of video games actually retrain their brains to be better at detecting fine details, tracking the movement of objects, paying attention, making decisions, understanding and manipulating multimedia, and many other behaviors that can be useful in the workforce.

That's right: one of the most engaging activities that the average person will ever experience is playing a video game. You might think that this statement applies only to persons under a certain age, but this is not true. According to Bavelier, ALL brains respond to the stimuli found in a well-designed computer game. The key is to find the right game—one that is loaded with the features that stimulate creativity, provides just the right amount of challenge, frustration and success, and pulls the participant into a world where they can interact with peers and be recognized for their achievements.

Making a game out of work

What can the study of game design teach us about engagement in the workplace? After all, you might be thinking, games are games and work is, well, work. The truth is, many organizations have already found ways to "gamify" the workplace, yielding measurable results in terms of employee engagement, which drives productivity and retention.

A recent study pointed to the trend toward the gamification of work, in an effort to make coming to work and doing a great job as addictive and self-motivating as the best video games. According to Gartner, more than 50 percent of companies that manage innovation processes will implement gamification in the workplace by 2015. Google is actually experimenting with turning engagement into an algorithm.

Getting started with gamification

It's not as simple as putting in a few foosball tables in the break room and making every day "casual Friday," however. Gamification is a design discipline which must be applied consistently if it is going to yield expected results. To start thinking about how to gamify your operation, take a look at an excellent presentation by Ralph Koster, one of the foremost authorities on game design in the world. You don't have to apply all of these techniques to be successful, nor should you. Just think about introducing a few of these components into your workplace and see what happens. If engagement goes up, you might add some additional components to your "game" later on. Here are just a few ideas to get you started:

- **Incorporate social networking.** One fundamental lever of video games is socialization. You can leverage social networking as a way r employees to recognize each other. This could mean "liking" the work of other employees, or linking to each other's work portfolios. Concerned about protecting your proprietary information? No worries; all of this can be done inside your firewall by using a variety of existing tools behind the firewall.

- **Reward with badges.** Badges have been proven to be effective to boost customer loyalty and engagement. If you think of your employees as your ultimate customers, let employees earn "badges" as a way to earn visible recognition for their contribution to the business.

- **Construct transparent compensation.** Making the compensation system transparent, so that employees know exactly how they can earn a raise or a bonus, can boost productivity by 7% and employee retention by 41%. Passing the "fairness test," a key component in game player engagement.

- **Balance teamwork and competition.** Experiment with the balance of competition and teamwork, since both components are highly engaging – but tend to cancel each other out if applied to excess.

- **Make results highly public.** Create a public scoreboard where employees can see instant performance results on an individual and team level, across the organization. The Association for Talent Development (ATD) has plenty of resources to help you get started with a balanced scorecard.

Engage your ultimate customer: employees

Remember that every employee is your ultimate customer. Each day, they truly wake up and make at least two crucial decisions:

- Will I come to work today?
- Will I put in my best effort or go through the motions?

How they answer will be influenced by a wide array of experiences and memories. And perhaps, how well you, as their leader, have decided to play the game.

Neuroscience and the Organization

References

• Society of Human Resource Management (SHRM),
www.shrm.org

• Laura Stack, TheProductivitypro.com, http://www.
theproductivitypro.com/FeaturedArticles/article00135.htm

• Kendra Cherry, What is Brain Plasticity? http://psychology.
about.com/od/biopsychology/f/brain-plasticity.htm

• Daphne Bavelier, Your brain on video games, http://www.ted.
com/talks/daphne_bavelier_your_brain_on_video_games

• Mark J. Nelson, Soviet and American Precursors to the
Gamification of Work, http://www.kmjn.org/publications/
Gamification_MT12.pdf

• Gartner Newsroom, Gartner Says By 2015, More Than 50
Percent of Organizations That Manage Innovation Processes
Will Gamify Those Processes, http://www.gartner.com/
newsroom/id/1629214

• Todd Ballowe, Google's Approach to Employee Engagement:
Surprise! It's an Algorithm, http://onstrategyhq.com/resources/
googles-approach-to-employee-engagement-surprise-its-an-
algorithm/

• Ralph Koster, How To: Properly Use Badges To Engage Customers,
http://mashable.com/2011/08/19/badges-gamification-tips/

• Shannon Ryan, Enterprise 2.0, Social networks behind
the firewall, http://www.slideshare.net/randywoods/
enterprise-20-social-networks-behind-the-firewall

• Corporate Executive Board, Boosting the Perceived Value
of Pay Through Transparent Communication, https://www.
cr.executiveboard.com/Public/CurrentResearch.aspx

• Tia Ghose, Chimps have a Sense of Fairness,
http://www.livescience.com/26245-chimps-value-fairness.html

- FinanceStore, Balancing the Dynamics of Teamwork and Competition, https://financestore.com/2011/09/02/balancing-the-dynamics-of-teamwork-and-competition/
- ClearAction.biz, Employee Engagement in Balanced Scorecards, http://clearaction.biz/blog/employee-engagement-balanced-scorecards-2/
- Association for Talent Development (ATD), www.atd.org

The Neuroscience of Virtual Instruction

In this series, we are exploring the practical application of neuroscience to education and training. Let's start by exploring the increasingly popular virtual instructor-led training (VILT). The Society of Applied Learning Technology (SALT) reports that "the vast majority" of companies plan to expand their use of VILT in the near future. Yet only 20 percent of these same companies find this delivery medium to be very effective.

So why do they keep doing it?

In the survey respondents say the primary reason is to save money. The next most-frequent response is reducing time away from the office, while the third reason is the ability to train large numbers of people quickly.

If you want to avoid investing time and money in training that is economical but ineffective, you might want to apply a little bit of science to your VILT programs. In this and subsequent articles, I'm going to discuss three areas of focus for enhancing the effectiveness of your VILTs: design, preparation, and follow-up. For now, let's start with design.

Design for engagement

Many VILTs follow a very predictable format. The first few minutes are spent getting organized and positioning participants online, followed by introducing the instructor and the topic. At the end of the class, there is usually a brief quiz or poll. The predictability of your programs may be causing your learners to tune out or multi-task instead of focusing.

This behavior occurs because the brain has developed pattern recognition as a survival mechanism. Our brain tends to relax in familiar surroundings and shifts into high alert in unfamiliar surroundings. Somewhere between feelings of boredom and anxiety is the highly productive level of attention. To help your VILT participants pay attention to you, design your VILTs for maximum engagement.

Here are a few ideas to get you started.

Jump into the content right away. Have you ever walked into a class or meeting a few minutes late and felt yourself scrambling to catch up with the conversation? If you start with content right away, your participants will be forced to pay attention immediately. There's also a secondary benefit: people will start logging in early to be sure they don't miss anything. This approach, on many television programs, attempts to engage views immediately so that they aren't tempted to switch channels while the predictable credits are showing. The credits eventually appear, several minutes into the program. You can do the same with your standard introductions.

Ask a challenging question in the chat window. While polls have their place, you'll get a lot more interaction from the use of the chat window. Pose a question that doesn't have a clear right or wrong or answer; then sit back while participants share their opinions. This simple tool helps your VILTs become social learning events in which participants learn from one another, not from the "the sage upon the stage."

Promote a participant to a presenter. When we watch someone else solve a problem or learn a new skill, mirror neurons fire in our brain in the same way as the person we're observing. We visualize ourselves in their place. A fascinating study demonstrated that students who watched others practice proper basketball free-throw techniques improved almost as much as those who were actually practicing. A very effective VILT technique is to have participants take turns trying a new skill. Let the rest of the class, rather than the instructor, provide help as needed to maximize the effect.

VILTs are here to stay. Designing them to be more engaging will help you get better results from your investment.

References

• Society of Applied Learning Technology (SALT), http://www.salt.org/salt.asp?ss=1

• General Physics Corporation, Delivering Virtual Instructor-Led Training (VILT), http://www.salt.org/weblink/industry/gp_trainingindustry_survey_results.pdf

• Michael Shermer, Patternicity: Finding Meaningful Patterns in Meaningless Noise, http://www.scientificamerican.com/article/patternicity-finding-meaningful-patterns/

• Carnegie Mellon University, Neuroscientists identify how the brain works to select what we (want to) see, http://www.sciencedaily.com/releases/2012/02/120221212618.htm

• Wikipedia, Cold open, http://en.wikipedia.org/wiki/Cold_open

• Kendra Cherry, How People Learn By Observation, http://psychology.about.com/od/developmentalpsychology/a/sociallearning.htm

• Association for Psychological Science, Monkey See, Monkey Do? The Role of Mirror Neurons in Human Behavior, http://www.psychologicalscience.org/index.php/news/releases/monkey-see-monkey-do-the-role-of-mirror-neurons-in-human-behavior.html

• Joe Haefner, Mental Rehearsal & Visualization: The Secret to Improving Your Game Without Touching a Basketball! http://www.breakthroughbasketball.com/mental/visualization.html

NEUROSCIENCE AND MARKETING
Why advertising works

Advertising is intended to drive behavior, such as purchase a product. Almost as soon as human beings started writing, they started advertising, by letting people know about events, products, and services in written form. From the very beginning, even though they didn't know it at the time, these early advertisers were applying neuroscience to their work—because nothing gets our attention at a conscious level without first engaging the brain.

Advertising works because it enlists our brain's bias for survival. When our species was just growing up, those of us who didn't pay attention to specific cues from the environment died before passing on our genes to offspring. Those of us who survived passed on our bias towards pattern recognition and over time we developed a brain that is programmed to alert us to changes that may indicate potential danger.

Today, our brain is still on the alert for threats to our survival. It evaluates all information in part on its value to keep you alive. You can actually watch the brain reacting to a television ad on YouTube. Notice where the eyes focus and the varying intensity of the electrical signals in the brain. The more intense the signal, the more engaged the brain is at the moment. Patrick Renvoise calls this approach "neuro-marketing."

Using neuroscience to promote learning

Nielsen, the advertising and marketing firm, has just opened a division entirely focused on applying neuroscience to advertising. The company is studying how consumers react to various offers, using brain scans and eye-tracking sensors to measure attention. They hope to be able to make advertising more targeted and effective for their clients by finding the optimal combination of text, images, and video that engage attention and foster the formation of long-term memory.

While you may not have the budget to hire them to create your Employee Learning Week campaign, there are a few things you can do to apply neuroscience to promote the value of organizational learning.

Tap into emotion. At its heart, all learning is emotional. The ventromedial prefrontal cortex plays a key part in making decisions of value, factoring in our emotional response to create a decision. You may find that using fewer facts and figures, and more images that can elicit an emotional response, such as pride, excitement, or even fear, will get your message more attention and be more memorable over time.

Tell a story. The brain is pre-wired to respond to stories. In fact, the brain can't really tell the difference between a story and the real experience. If an executive reads a vividly-told story about how another manager improved performance through training, his brain fires in the same places it would have fired if he had been the one going through the experience. A recent study showed that our brain processes information differently when told in a narrative. In summary, they found that the new neural pathways formed while reading the story are much more likely to persist, making it easier to remember information presented in story form.

Make it visual. Ninety percent of the information that enters the brain is visual. In fact, our verbal ability as a species is a relatively new skill when compared with the more deeply ingrained and more natural capability to process images. Look for a compelling way to get your numbers out in a visual manner by using infographics or other visual media. If you are making a presentation about your team's contributions, be sure to include relevant images that will make it easier for your audience to process critical information.

Build trust with consistent performance

We tend to reject information that does not come from a trusted source, so building a relationship with your audience is essential for selling them on the value of learning. Trust is registered in the caudate nucleus, a part of the brain that anticipates a reward and gives us, in advance, a hit of oxytocin. Oxytocin is linked to experiences such as "runners high" and sexual orgasm.

When we have decided to trust someone, we start rewarding ourselves for benefits we expect to receive, even before the actual benefit has been delivered. So the better you get at delivering value and communicating that value, the easier it will be communicate your value proposition going forward.

Send your message all year long

Our brains are constantly deciding where to focus attention and which experiences to commit to memory. For example, if you want the people in your organization to see the training department as a competitive advantage, you will need to keep up your advertising all year long, not just one week a year.

How We Make Logical Purchase Decisions (or not)

Think about the last major purchase decision you made. You probably conducted careful research, compared feature sets, searched for product reviews, sought out the opinion of friends and colleagues, and ultimately, made what you consider to be a logical decision. At least, that's how you felt during the process. But you might be surprised to learn that the brain processes emotional and purchasing decisions in the same place—making us question just how much emotion factors into any decision involving value.

Recently, two different research teams at Duke discovered that they were studying the same part of the brain to understand two brain functions that were previously thought to be completely unrelated: emotion and neuroeconomics. Neuroeconomics is a new field of study seeking insights into human economic behavior by studying the way the brain processes financial information and makes decisions about buying and selling.

Introducing the vmPFC

The region that is getting all this attention is the vmPFC (ventromedial prefrontal cortex), which is located between the eyes in the front of the brain. By watching this region in action while people are making decisions about value, scientists have discovered that it is active in making such decisions as: "Is this product or service really worth the price I would have to pay to acquire it?"

In answering questions about value, the vmPFC considers some expected factors, such as the cost of one product compared to a similar product with similar features, expected financial benefits from the acquisition and use of the product, and so forth. But it also factors in some less quantifiable considerations, including status, emotional satisfaction, excitement, and small rewards such as snacks or prizes.

So, did you buy that expensive human capital management application because it would give you more hard data about the effectiveness of your leadership development program, or because it would make you feel smarter than your peers? The answer is most likely a bit of both.

References

•Ashley Ross, The Evolution of Advertising: From Papyrus to YouTube, http://blogs.ubc.ca/etec540sept10/2010/11/29/the-evolution-of-advertising-from-papyrus-to-youtube/

•Sands Research Inc., Volkswagen - The Force.wmv, https://www.youtube.com/watch?v=V3s2zUvuM1g&noredirect=1

•Patrick Renvoise, Is There a Buy Button Inside the Brain: Patrick Renvoise at TEDxBend, https://www.youtube.com/watch?v=_rKceOe-Jr0&noredirect=1

•Nielsen, CONSUMER NEUROSCIENCE, http://www.nielsen.com/content/corporate/us/en/solutions/capabilities/consumer-neuroscience.html

•Wikipedia, Ventromedial prefrontal cortex, http://en.wikipedia.org/wiki/Ventromedial_prefrontal_cortex

•Susan Weinschenk Ph.D., Your Brain On Stories, https://www.psychologytoday.com/blog/brain-wise/201411/your-brain-stories

•Carol Clark, A novel look at how stories may change the brain, http://esciencecommons.blogspot.com/2013/12/a-novel-look-at-how-stories-may-change.html

•Lindsay Kolowich, Why Are Infographics So Darn Effective? http://blog.hubspot.com/marketing/effectiveness-infographics

•Robert Lane and Dr. Stephen Kosslyn, Show Me! What Brain Research Says About Visuals in PowerPoint, https://support.office.com/en-sg/article/

Show-Me-What-Brain-Research-Says-About-Visuals-in-
PowerPoint-8b802fd7-59d6-47c9-b4df-472aa5f18f09
•Mental_floss, What Makes Our Brains Feel Trust? http://
mentalfloss.com/article/54556/what-makes-our-brains-feel-trust
•Christopher Bergland, The Neurobiology of
the "Love Hormone" Revealed, https://www.
psychologytoday.com/blog/the-athletes-way/201308/
the-neurobiology-the-love-hormone-revealed
•Carnegie Mellon University, Neuroscientists identify how
the brain works to select what we (want to) see, http://www.
sciencedaily.com/releases/2012/02/120221212618.htm
•Duke University, Brain sets prices with emotional value, http://
www.sciencedaily.com/releases/2013/07/130702173156.htm
•Society for neuroeconomics, http://neuroeconomics.org/

The Neuroscience of Making a Decision

As early as 1994, some neuroscientists were making the case that emotions are a critical part of the brain's decision-making process. At that time, they discovered that a brain that has been injured and cannot feel emotions also cannot make a decision. Because emotions and logic are linked in our decision-making process, we must allow time for people to process the emotional content related to their decisions.

This fact has implications for change management, mentoring, coaching, purchasing, negotiating, and almost anything that we do as human capital managers. We need to make it safe for our subjects to experience and express emotions, and factor in these considerations in the decision-making process.

Permission to be emotional in the workplace

Every brain is different, but all of us react to our world with an integrated mixture of emotion and logic. There is no single combination of these two components that can be considered ideal, but understanding individual styles may help you predict their behavior in different situations. Expecting employees to check their emotions at the door is just plain silly, and leads to poor decisions, decreased productivity, and lost talent.

Beware of over-automation

There's a growing interest in using robotics and other automated processes to make many human capital decisions. While some of these applications may represent true advancement in our ability to interpret huge piles of data, I caution you to avoid eliminating emotion altogether from your decision-making process.

Consider the example of how Captain "Sully" Sullenberger let his "gut" and instinct help him make a life-and-death decision to land his plane on the Hudson rather than risk hundreds of fatalities if it had crashed on land. I encourage us all to make a decision right now to open our eyes to the possibilities of honoring the role of emotions in the making of even the most important life-and-death decisions.

Your future success as a human capital professional depends in part on how you decide to apply neuroscience to your work. Before you decide, ask yourself,

"How does this make me feel?"

References

• Antonio Damasio, Descartes' Error: Emotion, Reason, and the Human Brain

• Jenna Goudreau, The Emotional Life Of The Brain, http://www.forbes.com/sites/jennagoudreau/2012/04/26/the-emotional-life-of-the-brain/2/

• Linda Shiner, Sully's Tale, http://www.airspacemag.com/as-interview/aamps-interview-sullys-tale-53584029/?no-ist=

The Salesperson Effect

I've written elsewhere in this book about the role of the human brain to ensure survival. Man is a social animal, so a good part of our survival programming is focused on getting along well with other humans. In studies watching people think about future interactions with others, scientists have been able to actually see which parts of the brain are stimulated when a positive interaction is anticipated, versus the stimulation that occurs when thinking about an interaction that is believed will be negative or painful. While we are thinking about these possible events, our brains respond exactly as though the event were already taking place. So if we are thinking about something positive, our brain sends chemicals, including dopamine, that trigger a reward response—basically, that make us feel good. If we are envisioning a difficult conversation, however, our brain will trigger a response to stress or danger. We may feel anxious, fearful, or angry.

The neuroscience of influence

Another study has taken this idea a step further by observing brains trying to "sell" ideas to other people. One group was assigned the role of the "intern." Group members were told to bring movie ideas to members of the other group, the "producer," and convince these people to make movies from their ideas. Interns were assigned these ideas, which they were supposed to "sell."

By viewing a live MRI scan during the experiment, scientists discovered that they could accurately predict whether or not a producer would "buy" an idea by looking at two responses in the brain: anticipated reward and "the salesperson effect." If the intern believed that her idea would be accepted, her brain produced chemicals that delivered a positive feeling of success. She literally experienced her success in her mind before it happened. If the intern did not believe the idea would be accepted, it generally wasn't. This is pretty much what common sense might tell us, right? We've all been told that positive thinking yields better results than negative thinking, and this research confirms that intuitive belief.

The salesperson effect

Now the second factor gets very interesting. In addition to this "reward behavior predictor," scientists also found that some people were just more convincing than others. When these people spoke about their ideas, the same area of the brain was stimulated in the intern's brain and in the producer's. In other words, the presenter was able to trigger the reward stimulus in another person's brain. The scientists called this the "salesperson effect."

It is not clear if this effect is the result of some sort of innate ability or brain structure, or something that can be developed over time. Further studies likely will answer those questions. Soon it may be possible to hire salespeople by watching their MRIs as they attempt to sell something to another participant. We might be able to determine a leader's communication skills by measuring the strength of his salesperson effect on team members' brains. If we can discover the mechanism that is triggering this effect, we may be able to even train people to enhance this ability. Recruiters might be able to encourage applicants to be excited about their jobs, or the company that is hiring them.

References

• Christopher Harris, Dopamine and the Frontal Lobes,
https://www.youtube.com/watch?v=TI8-C9ZuLTA

- Anonymous, Stress Response in Animation, https://www.youtube.com/watch?v=BlfK0L8xDP0
- Deborah Kotz, Do you have the brain power to detect a hot idea and make it go viral?, http://www.boston.com/lifestyle/health/blogs/daily-dose/2013/07/10/you-have-the-brain-power-detect-hot-idea-and-make-viral/aGogFhtwqBzyKRV428aAyK/blog.html

Neuroscience and Marketing

The Herd Mentality

The "herd instinct" is an aspect of the leader-follower relationship that is illuminated by neuroscience. The neurochemical oxytocin triggers a "bliss response" in the brain whenever we are engaging in social behavior. The brain is an incredibly effective survival machine. One of our most successful survival techniques is our desire to find safety in numbers. When we belong to a group, this bliss response makes us feel warm, safe, and content. When we don't have a connection with a group, our brain triggers behavior that will compel us to seek new connections until we can get that bliss response again. In the last post I mentioned that oxytocin has been linked to such seemingly unrelated feelings as orgasm and motherhood. The good feeling that we get from belonging to a group is simply another manifestation of our response to engaging with other humans for survival.

Leaders should consider this herd instinct carefully to build followership:

1. **Recognize the power of existing affinities.** The "high" that we get from a flood of oxytocin can be habit-forming, possibly even addictive. This means that breaking out of our existing connections can be extremely difficult. Sociologists long have noted how difficult it can be for an individual to escape the influences of a teenage gang, and now we know that gang initiations actually can cause physical change in the brain, which makes it harder to break those bonds.

2. **Encourage the formation of new affinities.** If you want people to follow you, their brains must be able to recognize that they are part of a group of followers. Social media, face-to-face meetings, and other tools can help to send those signals to your followers' brains.

Brain Matters: How to help anyone learn anything using neuroscience

3. **Fight the herd instinct in yourself.** The paradox of all of this is that as a leader, you are in danger of falling into the herd mentality yourself. Leading often is uncomfortable, because you may not see other people around you doing similar things—that's because you are out in front of the pack. When you are leading, your brain will not release the chemical cocktail that makes you feel good. Instead, you may feel anxious and begin to doubt yourself. It will seem safer to run to another group, rather than to start your own.

The good news is that the herd mentality can be broken. Research shows that conscious choices can actually make physical changes in the brain, breaking established neural pathways and making it easier to form new ones. Leaders have to change two brains: their own and their followers. Understanding that fact might make it a little easier to deal with the herd instinct effectively.

References

•Ki Mae Heussner, Addicted to Love? It's Not You, It's Your Brain, http://abcnews.go.com/Technology/addicted-love-brain/story?id=11110866#.UeWq2lvn-kg

•Dr. Larry Mulkerin, Link seen in brains of soldiers, gang members, http://union-bulletin.com/news/2012/aug/17/link-seen-in-brains-of-soldiers-gang-members/

•Matthew Keener, You Can Change Your Brain: Matthew Keener at TEDxGrandviewAve, https://www.youtube.com/watch?v=QnCTrq5siac

Neuroscience and Marketing

Brain Matters: How to help anyone learn anything using neuroscience

ALL LEARNING IS EMOTIONAL

Snakes and the Brain

The Judeo-Christian story of the Garden of Eden tells us that the devil, disguised as a snake, tricks Adam and Eve into eating of the forbidden fruit on the Tree of Knowledge of Good and Evil. However, a recent study suggests that early, long-term exposure to snakes may have actually influenced the evolution of the human brain. Perhaps it's not just a story, after all.

Brain as a survival machine

Like all other life on this planet, humans evolved in order to survive, and our brains have become spectacular survival machines. By understanding the threats our earliest ancestors faced in our early history, we can understand why our brains function the way they do today.

For example, one theory suggests that the volatile ecosystem experienced by the earliest humans encouraged the development of adaptability to change. This ability came in handy when other species were dying out in the face of drastically changing climates, shifting tectonic plates, and other cataclysmic changes in the early days of life on earth.

One famous group of animals that failed to adapt, the dinosaurs, gave way to the small mammals that eventually gave birth to the primate line. But these small mammals had a fierce predator they had to face if they were going to survive and evolve into primates: the snake.

The snake response

Most of us will admit to having a fear of snakes, and we might also be a bit embarrassed—calling our feelings "irrational." However, research is building a compelling case that our brains are actually hard-wired to fear snakes, and that this trait came in handy when early primates were fighting for survival.

Anthropologist Lynne Isabel suspected that early mammals escaped being squeezed or poisoned to death by selecting for superior vision, enabling them to pick out a lurking snake. What makes her work especially interesting is that Dr. Isabel worked with neuroscientists to test her theory. The resulting study demonstrated that a group of macaque monkeys with no previous exposure to snakes reacted more strongly to snakes than to other stimuli.

This reaction has been attributed to evolutionary "hard wiring" that may have ensured the survival of early primates.

What's *your* snake response?

What other snake responses have made us who we are? What other hard-wiring are we going to discover deep inside our brains in the years to come? Do we have a survival instinct for appreciating beauty, loving family members, or believing in ourselves? As we come to know more about how each individual brain is wired, might there also be conclusions that can be drawn about organizations and societies? For example, will a work group that narrowly avoided multiple efforts to re-engineer it out of existence develop a group instinct for surviving down-sizing initiatives?

What else did the Book of Genesis get right? Maybe it's time we start reading it as natural history, rather than as a spiritual allegory.

References

• Wikipedia, Tree of the knowledge of good and evil, http://en.wikipedia.org/wiki/Tree_of_the_knowledge_of_good_and_evil
• Smithsonian National Museum of Natural History, Climate Effects on Human Evolution, http://humanorigins.si.edu/research/climate-research/effects
• Seth Borenstein, Tragedy for dinosaurs, opportunity for mammals, us, http://bigstory.ap.org/article/tragedy-dinosaurs-opportunity-mammals-us
• Lynne A. Isbell, The Monkey and the Snake: How the Primate Brain Reacts to Serpents, http://news.nationalgeographic.com/news/2013/10/131029-snakes-fear-primate-brain-neuroscience/

Your Emotional Brain

Neuroscientists have known for years that the human brain (as well those of other primates) is really multiple structures that have grown together through the process evolution. The oldest part of the brain is called the limbic system. This collection of structures in the brain is sometimes called our "survival center," because it controls autonomic functions, such as breathing, as well as the "fight or flight" response, which helps us react quickly when we are faced with a dangerous situation.

This same area of the brain is responsible for our emotional responses to the world. There was a time when the limbic system and the cerebral cortex were considered to be almost opposing sides of a debate, with the cerebral cortex representing rational thought and logic, while the limbic system represented irrational, raw emotion.

Television's *Big Bang Theory* recently featured this point of view as a boxing match. However, the reality is far more complex. In fact, we now know that these two parts of our brains work in tandem in the learning process.

Emotions are critical to learning

We've long known that emotions experienced during a learning event can intensify our memories and make them easier to access than non-emotional memories. For example, you may remember the face of the pretty girl who sat behind you in freshman algebra much better than you remember how to solve quadratic equations. The dark side of this linkage is demonstrated by post-traumatic stress disorder (PTSD), which can trap a victim in an endless loop of reliving a horrifying experience.

The link between emotions and learning goes even deeper, as research now indicates that an emotional response is actually critical to rationality. Our emotions play a key role in recognizing patterns, which is how the brain learns.

The brain also links different ideas and concepts based on how we feel about them, so without an emotional "tag," we will not be able to retrieve the information or apply it to new situations. In fact, Dr. Antonio Damasio has demonstrated that without emotions, no learning can take place. This means that, even if you haven't designed your training to elicit an emotional response, if it is effective, it is doing just that.

This begs the question: Why not make the linkage between emotions more intentional, so we can heighten the effect?

Putting emotions into learning

Here are a few ideas for putting emotions into learning that you may want to try in your next training or education event.

Ask yourself what emotional response you are targeting for your learners. How do you want them to feel as they implement the new skill you are covering? Structuring the learning event to trigger this target emotion will ensure that it is coded in the Cerebral Cortex for future use.

Remind learners of emotional events related to your subject matter. If you are teaching customer service skills, your message will be much stronger if you remind learners how they feel about poor vs. excellent service, rather than just reviewing best practices.

Deliver your message in a story. Our brains are highly empathetic to the experience of others. In fact, when we are watching events play out, our brains respond exactly as though we are experiencing the event ourselves. Instead of telling sales people how to handle objections, for example, tell them a story about a sales person who goes through the process with a customer. Be sure to highlight the salesperson's emotional response as she first fears that she will lose the sale all the way through to her elation when she closes the deal.

Introduce failure into your learning design. By putting learners in a situation where they may fail, you will be encouraging their emotional response to a challenge, motivating them to make an effort to learn and conquer the challenge. That feeling of accomplishment is much more powerful when it follows an initial failure.

Show learners how to be aware of emotions in the learning process. Try stopping your training delivery every so often and ask learners to what they are feeling. This practice will help them make those strong links between learning and emotion.

Surprise your learners. Our brains are hard-wired to be curious, so you creating an element of surprise will engage, delight and challenge your learners.

Talk to a teacher. While many of us in adult education need to be reminded of the emotional requirement in learning, you'll find many great ideas in the Kindergarten through twelfth grade (K-12) teaching community, when educators are more comfortable with consciously targeting an emotional response in support of the learning experience. If you want to get a better handle on how to leverage the power of emotions in your work as adult educator, seek out a great teacher and implement their best practices in your work.

How are you feeling right now?

Emotions are not distractions to learning; they are its key enablers. If I've been successful in stimulating critical thought in your brain, you should be feeling at least one emotion right now. Can you describe that feeling?

I'm also experiencing emotions as I write this post. And all of us are learning. I can almost feel the new pathways between neurons being formed in my brain. How about you?

References

•Shelley Uram, The Brain's Survival Mechanism; Humans vs Animals, http://www.shelleyuram.com/3448248.en.html
•Wikipedia, Cerebral cortex, http://en.wikipedia.org/wiki/Cerebral_cortex
•Big Bang Theory Transcripts, Series 6 Episode 03 – The Higgs Boson Observation, https://bigbangtrans.wordpress.com/series-6-episode-03-the-higgs-boson-observation/
•The Khan Academy, Emotions: Limbic System, https://www.youtube.com/watch?v=GDlDirzOSl8&noredirect=1
•Andrea Carolina Olave, Emotions are critical to patterning, https://prezi.com/xanjy8ex-nfg/emotions-are-critical-to-patterning/
•Jason Pontin, Hacking the Soul, http://www.technologyreview.com/qa/528151/the-importance-of-feelings/
•Tom Barrett, The DNA of an Explorer: How we are Hardwired to Question and Discover, http://edte.ch/blog/2014/03/19/the-dna-of-an-explorer-how-we-are-hardwired-to-question-and-discover/
•Robert Leanmnson, Teaching with Emotion: Approaches Across the Disciplines – SUCCESS in Teaching, Part 5, https://uminntilt.wordpress.com/2012/03/05/teaching-with-emotion-approaches-across-the-disciplines-success-in-teaching-part-5/
•Team Neuroplasticity, How the Brain Creates New Neural Pathways, http://www.whatisneuroplasticity.com/pathways.php

The Optimism Bias

A Google search for "optimism" will almost immediately retrieve information on neuroscientist Tali Sharot. In her book "The Optimism Bias," Sharot and others have found evidence that our brains are hard-wired to make optimistic predictions about our futures, even when the hard facts before us would indicate the contrary.

As Richard Dawkins convincingly states, our brains are survival machines, evolving the way they have precisely because they are very efficient at one critical task—keeping us alive. Perhaps having an optimistic outlook makes us more likely to survive. After all, optimism enables the brain to look ahead and imagine a future. It also makes us brave enough to explore or take a risk, expecting a positive result even when there is little reason to expect such an outcome. Without these life skills and cognitive strategies, our ancestors might have perished.

Your brain on optimism

Thanks to neuroimaging, scientists have identified the source of optimism, the caudate nucleus. This cluster of nerve cells that tells the rest of the brain when something good is about to happen.

Remember Skinner's dogs? Their caudate nucleuses were working overtime in those experiments. When these cells are communicating with other parts of the brain, we start to envision a positive future event.

But does an optimism bias really make a healthier or more productive workforce?

Up until about a month ago, I could have answered this question with a most confident and perhaps unrealistic "yes."

For the past 20 years or more, most of the literature seems to point out that having a generally positive expectation of the future contributes to a healthier body and greater productivity.

For example, college students whose thoughts were seeded with positive descriptions of their own abilities performed better on tests than those were given negative images of their own performance.

Not so fast, optimists!

But just when it seemed that we had a clear imperative: be optimistic or die too soon, a new study reveals that the opposite may be true. Adults over 65 who predicted a positive outlook for their future health tended to die sooner than those who expected their health to decline.

Hmm! I guess we need to do some more studying on how these neuropathways are affecting us. I'm sure neuroscientists will come up with a tie-breaker soon. Why do I say that? Is it just my unrealistically optimistic brain, spinning a vision of a more positive future than reason should allow? Or is it my relentlessly surviving brain, keeping me safe by giving me hope?

References

• Tali Sharot, The optimism bias,
http://www.ted.com/talks/tali_sharot_the_optimism_bias
• Richard Dawkins, The Selfish Gene: 30th Anniversary Edition,
http://www.amazon.com/The-Selfish-Gene-Edition-Introduction/dp/0199291152
• Wikipedia, Caudate nucleus,
http://en.wikipedia.org/wiki/Caudate_nucleus
• Wikipedia, B. F. Skinner, http://en.wikipedia.org/wiki/B._F._Skinner
• Sara L. Bengtsson, Raymond J. Dolan and Richard E. Passingham, Priming for self-esteem influences the monitoring

All Learning is Emotional

of one's own performance, http://www.ncbi.nlm.nih.gov/pmc/articles/PMC3150849/

•Sarah Kliff, Wipe that smile off your face, optimists: Science says you'll die sooner, http://www.washingtonpost.com/blogs/wonkblog/wp/2013/03/01/wipe-that-smile-off-your-face-optimists-science-says-youll-die-sooner/

HELPING PEOPLE LEARN

Why People Don't Pay Attention

Whether it's your spouse, your children, your boss, or your employees, at one time or another you've probably been frustrated because someone wasn't "paying attention" to you. We can take in thousands of bits of sensory data in seconds, cross-reference that data against the information stored in 140 billion brain cells in a micro-second, and retrieve memories of everything from a recipe, to our first date, to our current project plan from the same group of stimuli. And that's just what we are thinking about on the conscious level. Our brains simultaneously are signaling us to have emotional responses, which we may or may not be able to understand or even consciously recognize. At the unconscious level, our brains are making sure our bodies remember to do important, automatic things, like breathe and make our hearts beat.

Is it any wonder that sometimes our attention seems to wander?

The talent management professional is called upon to make presentations, write communication materials, or coach other people. Our effectiveness depends in part on our ability to draw and keep our audiences' attention. To be more effective "attention-grabbers," it helps to understand how attention works.

Through the technology of brain imaging, neuroscientists have discovered how our brain works to select what we actually see, by using some information and focusing on other data streaming into our brains through our vast sensory input. Here's how it works:

Our brain is built for survival. So it always is on the alert for potential danger and potential food. But the brain can't take it all in at once, so it has learned to be selective, bringing into focus only those stimuli that seem important for our survival. That's one reason why a sudden, loud sound will make us jump, and why we pay more attention to hamburger commercials when we're hungry.

Recent studies have shown that once the prefrontal cortex starts to focus on an object, it sends signals to the visual cortex, commanding the eyes to focus on that object. Soon, both parts of the brain are exchanging information. What is even more amazing is how they begin to oscillate in time with each other, showing the give-and-take of information as it is actually flowing between the two brain regions. We can also produce this effect by telling someone to focus on a particular object. Most brains will readily obey, apparently taking such instruction as a potential cue for survival.

Once a brain becomes focused on an object in this manner, all kinds of interesting things happen. Here's a few of them:

Change blindness. Studies show that once people are told to pay attention to a specific part of a scene or picture, they will fail to notice when even significant changes occur outside of the area of focus. One of the most interesting examples of this can be found on YouTube.

(Did you see the invisible gorilla the first time? I didn't.)

Short-term memory limitations. The brain holds new information in a special area called "short-term" or "working" memory. This is sort of like a temporary file in your brain. If the information is deemed valuable for survival, it is coded and cross-referenced with as much existing information as possible, so that we can retrieve it later. If it doesn't pass the "important to survival" test, it usually is discarded to make room for more incoming information. While our brains have an almost unlimited capacity to store information, this working memory is quite limited. Most studies say we can hold approximately:

- 1-5 images
- 5-9 digits
- 5-7 letters
- 4-6 words

If you want people to pay attention to you, here are a few tips:

- Tell them in advance what's important regarding what you are about to say.
- Keep the information coming in short chunks, to give the short-term memory time to process.
- Keep saying why this information is important, so that their brains will file the information away and make room for your next chunk of data.
- Link what you are saying to things they already know, to help the brain with the cross-referencing process.
- Include devices that the brain recognizes as potential changes in our survivability, such as:
  - movement
  - similarities
  - contrast
  - expected rewards
  - strong emotions

So the next time "they" aren't paying attention, ask yourself what *you're* missing.

References

• Carnegie Mellon University, Neuroscientists Identify How the Brain Works to Select What We (Want To) See, http://www.sciencedaily.com/releases/2012/02/120221212618.htm
• Indiana University, Change Blindness, http://cognitrn.psych.indiana.edu/CogsciSoftware/ChangeBlindness/
• Natalie Angier, Blind to Change, Even as it Stares Us in the Face, http://www.nytimes.com/2008/04/01/science/01angi.html?_r=1&
• Daniel Simons, selective attention test, https://www.youtube.com/watch?v=vJG698U2Mvo

The Brain on Change

There is nothing either good or bad but thinking makes it so."

—William Shakespeare

The first thing we need to understand about our brains and change is how our brain evolved. The human brain evolved to keep us safe in a dangerous world where our ancestors met deadly threats at every turn. In this world, survival didn't mean avoiding the next round of lay-offs; it meant avoiding being eaten by a tiger or mauled by a pack of wolves. Life was a short, constant battle to survive. And everything we are today was once a response to our need to survive.

In many ways, our brains—especially the more primitive parts—are still operating like they were back in those early days, constantly on the lookout for threats and responding with lightning speed to prepare us for fight or flight, our two most successful survival strategies.

Here's how it works. When the segment of your brain called the hypothalamus senses a threat to your survival, it triggers a series of physical responses:

- Your heart beats faster
- Your breathing speeds up
- Energy is released to your muscles
- Your sense of awareness is heightened

At the same time, sensory information has been sent to the hippocampus, which begins to analyze the information. The hippocampus will determine if it has seen this situation before and make a more fact-based determination of potential danger. If it looks like danger, signals are sent to the hypothalamus and the fear response is triggered or heightened. The amygdala will capture the context of this experience so that when we remember it in the future, we will recall the emotions and physical sensations surrounding the event. (That's how a significant childhood memory can be recalled with such rich, sensual detail.)

These and many other processes help your body prepare to fight or run like crazy. In today's world, these responses still help us to stay alive in true life-or-death situations. But they also can be triggered by perceived threats to our employment, self-esteem, or economic stability. And with each exposure to a potential threat, we store more information in the hippocampus, allowing us to use this information to evaluate the next threat that comes along.

For those of us who are responsible for change management, we need to consider how the brain responds to change.

Bias against change. Every change is a potential threat, and since it is much safer to assume that a change in our environment is a threat and act accordingly than to assume that it is positive, human beings have been hard-wired to react negatively to any and all change—at least until we receive more information.

Stress. With each successive change we become more alert to the patterns of change and what threats they may bring to our safety, our economic security, or our self-esteem. Employees can suffer from "change fatigue," a condition that looks like a mild form of Post-Traumatic Stress Disorder (PTSD). In a change fatigue state, the employee is experiencing stress, a condition brought on by repeated exposure to a fight or flight response. When the brain is under stress, our ability to think clearly and make decisions is greatly diminished. So it may be very difficult to reach employees who are in this state simply by explaining the facts to them—they are paying so much heightened attention to the potential threat that other messages have a hard time getting through to them.

Ironic process. Another byproduct of stress or severe mental overload is an interesting behavior by which we actually produce the results that we are trying the hardest to avoid. Golfers and other athletes understand this theory all too well. If we pay too much attention to the thing we are not supposed to do, this focuses our minds on that action so powerfully that we may almost feel compelled to do it. (I no longer tell myself, "Don't go into that sand trap" for this reason.)

Switch cost. Contrary to popular belief, the brain does not multitask. Instead, it switches between tasks. Each time the brain switches tasks there is a loss of performance. When the brain is allowed to stay on task, improvements in performance are demonstrated. When we are asking employees to do something differently, we are imposing switch cost on them. Even if we expect improved performance in the long run, we must prepare for reduced performance while the employee is making the switch.

References

•Dr. Joe Despenza, Look What Happens in Your Brain When You Change Your Mind, https://www.youtube.com/watch?v=Nmvk3zlyQ2w

•Dr. Norman Doidge, The Brain that Changes Itself, https://www.youtube.com/watch?v=t3TQopnNXBU

•Richard J. Davidson, Transform your Mind, Change your Brain. Google Tech Talks, https://www.youtube.com/watch?v=7tRdDqXgsJ0

•Julia Layton, How Fear Works, http://science.howstuffworks.com/life/inside-the-mind/emotions/fear.htm

The Growth Mindset

I sometimes like to think of the training profession as going through an evolution similar to the path taken by the medical science more than 300 years ago.

Before we knew about microbes and viruses, we knew that certain diseases affected the human body. Through trial and error, we discovered things that alleviated symptoms or even appeared to cure certain diseases. One day, scientists like Robert Hooke started using a new device, the microscope, to investigate the way tiny microbes behaved and affected larger organisms like the human body. Almost overnight, our understanding of disease and our power to cure it exploded.

We are going through a similar transformation with neuroscience. Using magnetic resonance imaging (MRI) and other imaging techniques, we can now study the structures and functions of the brain in real time. These new views give us deeper insights into how we learn, what obstacles prevent or hamper learning, and how we can restore brain function when something goes wrong.

Once we understood microbes, it wasn't long before the first vaccines were developed. Today, our emerging understanding of the brain has led to the discovery of the growth mindset—a powerful tool to help your employees become better learners.

What is the growth mindset?

In her book, Mindset, Dr. Carol Dweck shares her research into the different ways that people think about themselves and how these self-images affect our behavior and our ability to learn and adapt. She explains that there are two basic ways that we can view the world and our place in it.

A fixed mindset believes that our talents and abilities are fairly fixed at birth. This means that each of us has a hidden upper limit to what we can accomplish. People who have struggled in school may conclude, for example, that they just aren't cut out for college. So they end up in a low-paying, non-engaging job that doesn't stimulate their brain to form new connections. Their belief becomes reality because running that limiting statement over and over again created a very strongly enforced neural pathway, eventually reaching neurons connected to all parts of their lives.

On the other hand, an overly perfect "finished" view of oneself can be equally dangerous. This type of thinking establishes pathways that suggest that we are already perfect, so our brains become less adept and recognizing opportunities for improvement. Dweck identifies many CEOs and politicians with this type of thought pattern and it can lead to disastrous results when taken to the extreme.

To avoid becoming overly complacent about ourselves, educator Salman Khan recommends that we avoid telling our children how smart and accomplished they are and focus instead on their areas for growth. A word of caution here, though, this does not mean that we should start telling everyone how stupid or unskilled they are—that would just be another unproductive fixed mindset.

A growth mindset, on the other hand, is a belief that we never stop learning and improving. This mindset appears to actually encourage the growth of new neural pathways, forming new connections that weren't there yesterday, instead of running over the same pathway over and over again. Brains that are programmed to operate with this type of thinking tend to learn new information much faster. More importantly, they seem better able to connect one new thought or insight to another, allowing truly transformational ideas to emerge.

Neuroscience and the growth mindset

Much like the healers of prior days, psychologists used to have to infer how our mind works through observation and try to help us advance through trial and error. Today, we can actually test a theory like Dweck's against what we know about Neuroscience and see that it holds up.

The brain is constantly creating and destroying neural pathways, forming the thought and behavior patterns our brain uses to make decisions, choose actions and present us to the outside world. The pathways that are used get stronger; those that are under-used grow weak and eventually replaced.

When reviewed through this lens, Dweck's explanation of fixed vs. growth mindsets makes perfect sense—it correlates with hard scientific data. You can actually watch this process in action in this amazing video post from Camillia Matuk.

What does this mean to you?

As learning professionals, we have a shared responsibility to help our clients become the best learners possible. Helping employees adopt a growth mindset can make an organization more agile, more resilient, more creative, and even smarter. It is actually possible to use a growth mindset to enhance the Intelligence Quotient (IQ) of the individual and, by extension, the organization.

The good news is that you have already started to change the way your brain works, just by reading this article. Studies show that mere exposure to the concept initiates the formation of new neural pathways, even if you initially disagree with the premise. Our brains are pre-wired with a bias to learn new things. Somewhere along the way, some of us have actually learned to stop learning and we can unlearn those behaviors with conscious effort and repetition.

One simple way to encourage a growth mindset is to insert positive messages about everyone's capability to learn and change into every training intervention we produce. We can rewrite learning activities to make people fail more often, which is known to stimulate much more neural activity than the successful completion of a new task. Finally, we can partner with leadership to encourage a new way of looking at ourselves and our employees as works in progress, rather than fully defined blocks with "strengths" and "weaknesses."

A friend of mine has a credo that she shares and lives by: Learn something new every day. In a nutshell, that's a sound plan for growth.

References

•Wikipedia, Robert Hooke, http://en.wikipedia.org/wiki/Robert_Hooke

•Wikipedia, Magnetic resonance imaging, http://en.wikipedia.org/wiki/Magnetic_resonance_imaging

•Dr. Carol Dweck, Mindset, http://mindsetonline.com/index.html

•Salman Khan, The Learning Myth: Why I'll Never Tell My Son He's Smart, https://www.khanacademy.org/about/blog/post/95208400815/the-learning-myth-why-ill-never-tell-my-son-hes?utm_source=Sailthru&utm_medium=email&utm_term=All%20Coaches&utm_campaign=Sal%20Op-ed%20Email%20%28Coaches%29

•Camillia Matuk, The Plastic Brain (full animation), https://www.youtube.com/watch?v=8Vo-rcVMgbI&noredirect=1

•Association for Psychological Science, Improving Intelligence, http://www.psychologicalscience.org/index.php/publications/observer/2011/july-august-11/improving-intelligence.html

•Russell Poldrack, Novelty and Testing: When the Brain Learns and Why It Forgets, http://niemanreports.org/articles/novelty-and-testing-when-the-brain-learns-and-why-it-forgets/

•Jeanette Norden, The Neuroscience of Learning and Memory, https://www.youtube.com/watch?v=wtu-yAm4xik

Brain Matters: How to help anyone learn anything using neuroscience

EXPLORING INTELLIGENCE

What does it Mean to be Intelligent?

The Singularity is a term you'll find in science and in science fiction. It was coined by mathematician John von Neumann to define a theoretical moment when the artificial intelligence of computers surpasses the capacity of the human brain. The term is borrowed from physics and quantum mechanics, where the term gravitational singularity is used in the study of black holes. These events are all considered singular because we are unable to predict what happens next; the disruptive degree of change associated with the event is simply too great for our current body of knowledge.

While we are far from attaining the goal of artificial intelligence, there was a brief flurry of excitement recently when a computer passed the Turing Test, to mixed reviews. In this post, we'll talk about the Turing test, how computers are already augmenting human cognition, and what it may mean to the learning profession.

The Turing Test and the Definition of Artificial Intelligence

Alan Turing was a code-breaker in World War Two and a pioneer in digital computing. He posited that it would one day be possible to build a computer that would be able to behave much like a human. Specifically, he believed it would be able to learn, and to apply that learning to solve problems beyond its program. He suggested that the best way to recognize success - the singularity some people speak of today - was to put the computer to a test. Engage the computer in a conversation with multiple users for an extended period of time. If the computer convinces at least 30% of the users that they are communicating with a "real person," the computer passes the test. While some have suggested that it is time to update the Turing Test, it still excites us when a computer comes close to passing. Want to see how one person interacted with this "intelligent" computer program? Read this interesting transcript and decide for yourself.

Augmented Cognition – The Flip Side of Artificial Intelligence

While computer scientists will continue to pursue true artificial intelligence, another area of exploration is yielding more immediate returns. Augmented Cognition is the use of neuroscience to determine a subject's cognitive state in order to enhance it, usually with computers. To me, this is the flip side of Artificial Intelligence. Instead of trying to make a computer act like the human brain, we try to make our brains a bit more like computers.

The U.S. Defense Advanced Research Project Agency (DARPA) has been interested in this technology for years. Samsung is developing a device to enable people to operate a computer through brain signals. Honeywell has developed a prototype helmet that monitors brain states associated with distraction and information overload. The system produces a visual readout to help commanders understand the cognitive patterns of individual soldiers. Researchers at the University of

California (UC), San Francisco, and UC San Diego are watching the brain of a volunteer in real-time as she opens and closes her eyes and hands. They hope to understand how her brain transmits these commands. On my desk right now, there's a headset called MindWave. I use this headset to monitor my own brainwaves and maybe eventually control them. Teachers are starting to use a similar technology to study how students learn. With such devices, we might be able to identify the state that Csikszentmihalyi called "flow." This state is often described as a feeling of hyper-learning and well-being.

In other words, by marrying our brains to computers, human beings may become the Singularity.

Where Do We Go From Here?

It is hard to say when the Singularity will occur, or whether we will even recognize it when it happens. It may be that our convergence with computers is so gradual that we never see a sharp line, but more of a gradual blending — like colors turning from one shade to another. When does blue become blue-green? When does the brain become a biological computer?

As learning professionals, we need to think about how we can use these new technologies to help people learn faster, perform better, retain memories longer, and hopefully become more human in the process.

The Internet of Everything Is Us

It has been said that we are living in the era of the Internet of Everything, meaning that everything will become smarter through connection to the Internet. I'm not sure that the authors of this term realized they were not just talking about toasters and automobiles.

They were talking about themselves.

References

- Wikipedia, Technological singularity, http://en.wikipedia.org/wiki/Technological_singularity
- Tom Harris, Robots and Artificial Intelligence, http://science.howstuffworks.com/robot6.htm
- Kimberly Ruble, Computer Program Passed the Turing Test, http://guardianlv.com/2014/06/computer-program-passed-the-turing-test/
- Gregory Baskin, Alan Turing the Father of Computing, http://guardianlv.com/2014/06/alan-turing-the-father-of-computing/
- Joshua Batson, Forget the Turing Test: Here's How We Could Actually Measure AI, http://www.wired.com/2014/06/beyond-the-turing-test/
- Deb Amlen, Our Interview with Turing Test Winner 'Eugene Goostman,' https://www.yahoo.com/tech/our-interview-with-turing-test-winner-eugene-goostman-88482732919.html
- Honeywell, Body-mounted sensors monitor brain and heart activity to prevent information overload and keep soldiers out of harm's way, http://www.honeywell.com/sites/honeywell/featuredproduct_cat181ec08-fbba81b57b-3e3e4447ab3472a0c2a5e5fdc1e6517d_H99789C49-39C9-5D90-CB9E-E96FE0C5FB3B.htm
- Carl Zimmer, Flying Through Inner Space, http://phenomena.nationalgeographic.com/2014/03/19/flying-through-inner-space/
- EduTech Wiki, Flow theory, http://edutechwiki.unige.ch/en/Flow_theory

The High Cost of Being Smart

I've said previously that the brain is a survival machine, which evolved specifically to keep us alive. You might think that because the human brain is considered to be the most complex brain, it is superior in all respects to those of other animals. However, because each of these brains are survival machines for their respective species, they have developed in ways that give each animal unique competitive advantages.

The differences between animal brains and our own can give us a glimpse of evolutionary roads we as a species have yet to travel. And, as we develop the technology to augment our own cognition, these animal brains might give us a bit of a "shopping list" for the next wave of evolution.

Take a look at a few of these capabilities and see if you would like to add them to your brain's already powerful toolkit.

Cats are almost always in alpha mode

Cats seem to spend most of their waking hours in a predominantly alpha mode, meaning that their visual cortex exhibits a higher degree of alpha waves than humans. In some studies, these particular waves have been linked with transcendental meditation and psychic phenomena or intuition.

Dogs are more empathetic

In a recent study, dogs were placed in a room with two people, one quiet and one openly crying. Over and over again, the dogs sought out the crying person and appeared to try and console them. What do you think would happen if we tried this same experiment on humans?

Chimps are better at game theory

A study performed at the Indianapolis zoo indicates that chimps perform better than us in certain games where a combination of cooperation and competition are required to win.

Horses "talk" with their ears

A recent study of horses revealed a far richer social life than you might expect, as they communicate with each other through facial expression, especially the movements of their eyes and ears. While some humans can learn how to wiggle their ears, our use of these appendages as a communication vehicle seems to be a missed opportunity along our evolutionary path.

Whales and elephants express grief

Whales and elephants have demonstrated strong emotional attachments to each other and to their group, even after years of separation. Elephants in particular demonstrate behavior that appears to mirror human grief and self-awareness. It is believed that mirror neurons, once thought to be unique to the human brain, is responsible for this ability in the brains of elephants, whales, dolphins and humans.

Bees have a better sense of direction

Even the honey bee, with a tiny brain comprising only about 950,000 neurons versus our 1 billion, has developed an extraordinary talent. Bee neurons are highly specialized, giving it navigational skills that have been proven to be more accurate than Global Positioning Satellites (GPS). Bee brains have developed a combination of a solar compass and internal clock to determine the bee's relationship to the sun and the length of time she has been flying from the hive. While the bee brain doesn't have the extensive structures for memory exhibited by human brains, it is able to remember the precise location of a food source or a likely location for a new hive long enough to communicate that location in great detail in the form of a "waggle dance."

Science fiction or science future?

The Expensive Tissue Hypothesis suggests that as the human brain grows larger and requires more energy, we give up certain other survival advantages in favor of pursuing our singularly spectacular survival tool. It's sort of like when a promising young baseball pitcher spends so much time practicing his fastball that his batting average suffers through lack of practice. If he's a good enough pitcher, no one really cares.

But what if we could really have it all? What if we could go back into time and pick up those evolutionary detours we bypassed on the way to being human? Is it crazy science fiction to believe that we may one day adopt some of these capabilities to augment our own performance?

Yetkin and Berber suggested the bee's "swarm mentality" algorithm might become a more accurate replacement for today's GPS system. In this book, we have suggested that augmented cognition may change the nature of work and our ability to perform it in our own lifetimes.

Still, neuroscience and its applications for learning are still in the early stages of development. We are only beginning to understand what we gave up to become us.

References

• John Medina, Brain Rules, http://www.brainrules.net/survival
• M. Chatila, C. Milleret, P. Buser, A. Rougeul, A 10 Hz "alpha-like" rhythm in the visual cortex of the waking cat, http://www.sciencedirect.com/science/article/pii/001346949290147A

Exploring Intelligence

• Stephanie Pappas, Canine Comfort: Do Dogs Know When You're Sad? http://www.livescience.com/20823-canine-comfort-dogs-understand-emotion.html

• Christopher Flynn Martin, Rahul Bhui, Peter Bossaerts, Tetsuro Matsuzawa & Colin Camerer, Chimpanzee choice rates in competitive games match equilibrium game theory predictions, http://www.nature.com/srep/2014/140605/srep05182/full/srep05182.html

• EarthSky, Horses communicate with expressive eyes and mobile ears, http://earthsky.org/earth/horses-communicate-with-expressive-eyes-and-mobile-ears?utm_source=EarthSky+News&utm_campaign=484b4498a2-EarthSky_News&utm_medium=email&utm_term=0_c643945d79-484b4498a2-393695381

• XiXi Yang, How To Wiggle Your Ears, https://www.youtube.com/watch?v=mHZd1SFAGck&noredirect=1

• Chalkimation, Episode 9: The True Story of Whale Brains, https://www.youtube.com/watch?v=qr2cWHJt0Go&noredirect=1

• BBCWorldwide, Elephants grieving - BBC wildlife, https://www.youtube.com/atch?v=C5RiHTSXK2A&list=PLGUycDPAJepa7kVwtxkMwod9t QyrYaJWe&noredirect=1

• University of California Television (UCTV), CARTA: Theory of Mind--What Makes Humans Different? Brain Imaging Studies Mirror Neurons and More, https://www.youtube.com/watch?v=RfLWmhYjPTQ&noredirect=1

• Elizabeth Pennisi, In the battle for fitness, being smart doesn't always pay, http://www.sciencemagazinedigital.org/sciencemagazine/08_august_2014?sub_id=zsVHk2ZbfEUt&folio=609#pg13

• Tracy V. Wilson, Dinner and Dancing: Bee Navigation, http://www.howstuffworks.com/insects/bee5.htm

• Georgia Tech College of Computing, The Waggle Dance of the Honeybee, https://www.youtube.com/watch?v=bFDGPgXtK-U&noredirect=1

• Mevlut Yetkin, Mustafa Berber, Implementation of robust estimation in GPS networks using the Artificial Bee Colony algorithm, http://connection.ebscohost.com/c/articles/94609442/implementation-robust-estimation-gps-networks-using-artificial-bee-colony-algorithm

Multiple Intelligence
in the Classroom

Combining what we know about multiple intelligences with virtual classroom features can help us enrich e-learners' experiences. This article originally appeared in ATD Learning Circuits and is reprinted with permission.

Howard Gardner, creator of the theory of multiple intelligences (MI), alerted us to the different ways people process information and the importance of taking those differences into account when designing learning events. You may have modified the activities in your traditional classroom based on multiple intelligences theory, but what about your virtual classroom? In many companies, 50 percent or more of the curriculum is now offered in some form of collaborative virtual classroom. However, much of that material appears to be little more than PowerPoint slides with audio of the instructor's voice. Often, companies assume that this limited approach is all that's possible with existing technology. But many more features exist in a virtual classroom, and combining these with what we know about MI can help us enrich e-learners' experiences. Here's how.

Use all of the available features

There are dozens of major virtual classroom providers and hundreds of companies that resell the classrooms under a private label arrangement. Once you select the right virtual classroom for your needs and budget, you can begin to design learning events and programs that take advantage of the available features. These features vary a bit from provider to provider, but most providers offer the ability to

- display presentations, such as PowerPoint slide shows
- share the facilitator's desktop or an application
- use a whiteboard for drawing and charting
- hold conversations in chat rooms or sub-chat rooms
- create voice sub-conferences, often called breakout rooms
- document and slide markup tools, such as highlighters and text or drawing tools
- administer surveys and quizzes
- download documents and reference materials
- connect to URLs on the Internet or an intranet
- use symbols, sometimes called emoticons, to show emotions and raise questions

Plan to engage as many different intelligences as possible

Once you're familiar with the features in your virtual classroom, plan your learning event or program to engage as many different intelligences as possible, using all of those features. As you review the list of suggestions below, remember that we all have these capabilities to some degree, but each of us will be stronger in some areas and weaker in others. The best way to ensure that you're engaging as many learners as possible to the greatest degree possible is to use as many different ways to appeal to those multiple intelligences as the technology will allow. Here are a few ideas, listed by intelligence type, to get you started.

Visual/spatial intelligence. People with a strong visual capacity tend to create pictures in their minds to represent thoughts or concepts. These learners respond particularly well to learning activities that let them

- see key points demonstrated with detailed graphics or visual effects, such as in a PowerPoint presentation
- watch a video of a process or a story that pertains to the course (No talking heads, please!)

- interpret and apply charts that summarize statistics
- use flow charts or maps to arrive at a solution or destination
- interpret visual puns or metaphors that capture a key fact or concept
- share mind-mapping software or graphic organizers to understand a problem or collaborate on a solution
- design, draw on, modify, or correct a diagram using a whiteboard and digital markup tools

Verbal/linguistic intelligence. People with highly developed speaking and listening skills often think in words rather than in pictures. These learners will respond particularly well to activities such as

- listening to or telling stories that illustrate a key learning point
- taking detailed notes during a lecture
- reading and interpreting text
- selecting and advocating a course of action
- memorizing key facts or dates
- analyzing case studies
- exchanging typed ideas and information with the instructor or other learners in a chat room
- answering written quizzes or surveys based on facts

Logical/mathematical intelligence. People with a highly developed ability to use reason, logic, and numbers tend to think by using patterns and linking concepts. These learners always like to ask a lot of questions and expect detailed answers to help them link pieces of information together.

They may benefit from learning activities such as:

- working on a spreadsheet or calculating percentages or metrics with other learners
- conducting or analyzing an experiment
- interviewing an instructor or subject matter expert to get the answer to a problem

- classifying or organizing separate items into larger groups
- developing theories or conclusions based on facts in evidence
- solving a problem expressed as a crime or mystery

Bodily/kinesthetic intelligence. These people have a highly developed ability to control body movements and handle physical objects. They process information by interacting with the physical space around them. Because the space around them is virtual, you'll have to create virtual interactions to help these people use their intelligence effectively. They will respond well to learning activities involving

- hands-on manipulation of the keyboard or mouse as a "student driver"
- watching videos or presentations that let learners put themselves in the action
- simulations that let learners make decisions that affect the outcome of the story or case
- game-like activities that require hand-to-eye coordination or rapid reflexes
- buttons that let them express feelings with digital signals that take the place of facial expressions
- videoconferencing that lets them show their body to other participants and express concepts through gestures, mime, or dance
- blended solutions that let them create something with their hands and share it with the rest of the class through a digital image

Musical/rhythmical intelligence. Learners with a heightened ability to appreciate and produce music tend to think in sounds, rhythms, and patterns. They're also extremely sensitive to environmental sounds that might be interpreted only as background noise by other learners.

Try some of these activities to engage these learners:

- compose or ask them to compose a song or rap to summarize key points
- associate tones with different stages of a process, different eras in time, or different levels of performance
- use sound effects to accentuate the key points in a presentation
- play subtle background music to enhance the desired mood (excitement, deep thought, relaxation, and so forth)

Interpersonal intelligence. Learners with an advanced ability to relate to and understand the feelings of other people often process information by linking it to a story about how other people feel in a given situation. They enjoy learning in a team setting, working with other people, and possibly taking a leadership role.

Activities for interpersonal intelligence include:

- creating sub-conference groups to allow for small group discussion
- role-playing the same case from several different points of view
- analyzing case studies for motivations, conflict, feelings, or intentions
- using verbal skills to build consensus or agreement

Intrapersonal intelligence. People dominant in intrapersonal intelligence exhibit a strong sense of self and the ability to understand and share their inner thoughts and feelings. These people process information by reflecting on their own strengths and weaknesses, establishing dreams and goals, and understanding their relationships with others. Intrapersonal learning activities might include:

- surveys that focus on how the learner feels about a particular subject or fact

- role play showing their own responses or emotions in a particular setting or scenario
- discussion of how the actions of others make them feel or think
- retracing how they solved a problem or learned a new skill and applying that process to a new learning situation

Naturalist intelligence. People with a heightened appreciation for and understanding of the world around them like to experience the outdoors and relate well to animals. They tend to process information best by exploration. These learners will respond well to activities that let them:

- visit other Websites or resource documents and investigate a topic on their own
- organize and conduct a virtual field trip to show sites that have interested them to other learners
- go on a virtual tour of a company site, library, or museum
- create blended learning that combines live field trips with sharing those experiences in the virtual classroom

Put it all together

Remember that everyone exhibits a combination of the various intelligences. The goal is to engage as many of these different capacities as possible within the same learning event or program. Too often, we find that inexperienced instructional designers use one particular activity and continue to repeat it exclusively, when other types of meaningful activities would create more variety, increase learner interest, and appeal to multiple learning styles.

For example, in a project management course, you could use a small group discussion followed by a visual activity such as a collaborative flow chart. Later, you could bring the entire class to a Website to explore project management principles and resources.

Build a library of learning activities. As you begin to deploy your virtual classroom, you will build a curriculum of learning programs that you have designed specifically for this environment. In addition to leveraging reusable learning objects, be sure to build a database of reusable learning events and activities. This approach will save you time as your virtual classroom curriculum continues to grow.

Assess your own intelligences. It's natural to develop an unconscious bias that reflects your own areas of intelligence. By taking a self-assessment, you can learn more about your preferences for one form of delivery over another and work to establish more balance in your approach.

By paying attention to the multiple intelligences of your audience, you'll find that your learning programs are more exciting and more effective. As you grow more comfortable with the technology, your own creativity will begin to respond to the challenge. Use these simple suggestions to help you get started.

References

• LdPrice.net, Learning Styles Test,
http://www.ldpride.net/learningstyles.MI.htm.
• Walter McKenzie, I think … therefore … MI!
http://surfaquarium.com/MI.

Is the Workforce Getting Less Intelligent?

Consider the implications of a recent study on workforce skills by the Organization for Economic Cooperation and Development that looks how literacy, numeracy, and problem-solving is used at work. Compared to other populations, U.S. adults scored toward the bottom in every category tested.

Even more concerning to those of us who take a global view of things, however, was the fact that just about everyone did worse than expected. If the study were not grading on a curve, there would be no winners. Everyone is still stumbling, and yet, acquisition of these very simple skills has been directly linked to jobs and economic success.

Perhaps even more troubling is the finding that the adult children of less educated parents are much more likely to be lower-skilled and less-educated themselves. In the United States, this trend is more pronounced than in almost every other industrialized nation. According to Don Tapscott and others, we are creating a world of have and have-nots with regards to basic 21st century survival skills.

Skills gap revisited

ATD called out this issue almost a decade ago with its first Skills Gap whitepaper, published in 2004. Since then, the organization has updated this information on a regular basis. U.S. businesses are well aware of the lack of skilled labor in the American workforce. Hundreds of books on the subject have been written and countless panels convened. And yet the issue continues to slow down our economy and lock millions out of an economically secure future.

Is the Internet to blame?

Parents have long suspected that countless hours spent online are making their teenagers lazy and less intelligent. Until recently, I would have completely disagreed with this position, arguing that the Internet is exposing those teenagers to global thought leaders, new ideas, and challenges, as well as helping them develop critical computer-based skills.

Is our brain remaking itself into a less intelligent version of itself?

In the popular press, the word "intelligent" is often misused, and I have intentionally used this word in order to get your attention. When we talk about people being less *educated* or less *skilled* than they should be, we immediately start looking for solutions and assume that we will find them.

But being less *intelligent* is a harder problem to solve— because it implies that there is a fundamental lack of ability that is inherent in the individual's makeup. We all know about Howard Gardner's theory of multiple intelligences, but have you read Isaac Asimov's essay, "What is Intelligence?" He gets to the same idea in a lot fewer words.

So, are we really becoming less intelligent? If this is true, it would mean that our constantly evolving brains are actually going backward in some physical, evolutionary way. One theory is that, while we are constantly creating new neural connections, these connections are increasingly linking highly superficial bits of information (such as who won last year's latest talent competition) rather than developing new knowledge that can help us in the workplace.

Making the workforce more intelligent

In the face of this frightening downward spiral of human capability, what's a human capital manager to do? One strategy is to shore up fading cognitive skills with performance support tools and technology.

You could also start offering classes in basic reading, math, and problem-solving in your place of business. These are probably both great ideas and things you should consider in the short-term. I'd like to suggest another more long-term approach as well.

Learning to learn

The number one reason that mankind has survived to this point has been the spectacular biological competitive advantage that sits between our ears. So, if our brains are being dumbed-down by the digital age, let's put our brains to work and reverse the process.

Instead of merely plugging the holes in our understanding and skill, let's start teaching people how to teach themselves. Learning to learn started as a strategy to help students with learning disabilities. Over time, some educators have come to realize that simply being alive in the 21st century brings with it a set of learning disabilities that must be overcome through conscious effort, practice, and education in how our brains work. If you want to reverse the trend toward a less-intelligent workforce, you have the power to do so.

Start making yourself a little smarter today: Read a book, solve a problem without Googling the answer, or learn a new practical skill. Your brain will thank you.

References

•Organization for Economic Cooperation and Development, Boosting skills essential for tackling joblessness and improving well-being, http://www.oecd.org/newsroom/boosting-skills-essential-for-tackling-joblessness-and-improving-well-being.htm

• World Future Society, World Future Review interviews Don Tapscott, author of Grown Up Digital, http://www.wfs.org/node/714

• Association for Talent Development (ATD), Bridging the Skills Gap: How the Skills Shortage Threatens Growth and Competitiveness...and What to Do About It, http://books.google.com/books/about/Bridging_the_Skills_Gap.html?id=rduOD5uEuEMC

• Isaac Asimov, What is Intelligence? http://www.is.wayne.edu/MNISSANI/20302005/IQAsimov.htm

• Wikipedia, Evolution of human intelligence, http://en.wikipedia.org/wiki/Evolution_of_human_intelligence

• Neurobonkers, The lesson you never got taught in school: How to learn! http://bigthink.com/neurobonkers/assessing-the-evidence-for-the-one-thing-you-never-get-taught-in-school-how-to-learn

THE BRAIN AND LANGUAGE

What's in a Name?

You know the quotation from Shakespeare: "What's in a name? That which we call a rose by any other name would smell as sweet." But our brains might process the sensation of smelling that rose differently if we named it something else.

The power of names

Verbal abilities are a relatively recent development for our brains. But once we got the hang of it, we started using names as a shorthand way of retrieving all manner of memories, images, sensations, emotions, and even autonomic physical responses. The Old Testament (Genesis 2:20) says that God brought all the animals to Adam and asked him to name them, and we have been naming our world since then.

Name recognition and self-awareness

Babies learn to respond to their own names at a very early age— perhaps even before birth. But we aren't the only creatures who associate unique meanings to our own names. We have all seen a pet respond to the name provided by their owners, mimicking Adam's process of naming the animals in the Garden of Eden.

But many animals have been shown to use unique signatures when communicating with each other. Parrots and primates name their children. Dolphins and whales also seem to name each other, and remember unique individuals by a specific set of sounds even years after their last encounter with the individual.

So what is happening in the brain when we (and our fellow animals) process our own names? It turns out that the Shakespeare may have gotten this one wrong; a rose by any other name would certainly have the same chemical signature, but our brains would likely assign different associations to the object if we named it differently.

Try it yourself. Picture a rose, but call it a "stink weed" in your head. Here's what is happening: Our brains are made up of specialized cells, called neurons. When these neurons change their electro-chemical state, we experience a brain event, like solving a puzzle or recognizing our own names. After a certain period of time, our names are held in long-term memory for repeated use.

But while a baby is learning, he needs reinforcement to tell the brain to keep this bit of data in long-term memory. And over time, we also associate a rich web of cross-referenced sensations, emotions, and other bits of data into a deep-seated concept of self that is uniquely tied to our name.

We follow a similar process with each and every word we learn, making language the symbolic code that the brain uses to organize conscious thought.

Social and economic impact of names

Consider our own names. Because so much information is coded against a name, that word we use to describe ourselves can have unintended consequences. While parents choose names for their children for mostly personal reasons, their choices reflect society in many subtle ways. In addition, a child's name can have positive or negative effects on social status and income later in life.

What names does your organization use?

By applying this research to the field of human capital management, we can see that the name you assign to an employee can affect the way they feel about the organization, as well as the way that others feel about them.

Take my name for example. I am often assigned an email address using my full first name, "Marjorie," instead of the name I call myself, "Margie." From that point on, my interactions with my co-workers are shaped by their associations with "Marjorie." However, I feel that I am not being called by the label that symbolizes my understanding of "me."

How hard would it be to let employees exercise this fundamental right of choosing their organization name? Some companies, such as Bank of America and Disney, have chosen to call their employees by more descriptive names. There is a different reaction when we are called "associates," partners," or "characters." These companies are applying sound brain science in choosing theses names carefully.

Indeed, Dale Carnegie recognized the power of a name when he advised readers to learn a man's name and use it frequently if we want to influence him.

To be sure, a rose is a rose is a rose. But by any other name, it would likely be something else altogether.

References

• Terrence Deacon, Ph.D., The Co-evolution of Language and the Brain, http://www.childrenofthecode.org/interviews/deacon.htm

The Brain and Language

• Corrine Caputo, A Look Into How Pop Culture Influences Our Baby Names and Where I Want It To Go From Here, http://hellogiggles.com/a-look-into-how-pop-culture-influences-our-baby-names-and-where-i-want-it-to-go-from-here

Words and the Brain

The human brain has evolved over six millions years. The most primitive parts of our brain operate at a deeply unconscious level, and influence a great deal more of our conscious behavior than most of us realize. As we added more complex structures to support critical thought, reasoning, language, and social behavior, our frontal lobe grew larger to accommodate a great workload. However, this part of the brain continues to be cross-wired with the more primitive structures that support survival. This is a simplified explanation of why a dispute at work can generate a "fight or flight" response when our physical survival is not even remotely threatened.

While the precise language timeline is hard for science to pin down, our capacity for language developed only recently. And yet, language doesn't operate simply at the newer, conscious level of the brain. We respond to words at a visceral, autonomic level as well. Understanding the impact of words on the brain can help us to become better managers, parents, negotiators—almost any other role in which we as human capital professionals may find ourselves.

Prime the brain with words

The University of Georgia is teaching lawyers how to use words to prepare clients for mediation. Harvard is studying the effect of using positive words or images, such as those related to rewards, victory, or security, at the start of a negotiation, rather than focusing on the items in dispute. This priming can trigger the production of oxytocin, the neurochemical that helps trigger feelings such as well-being, affinity, and security. Change management plans might be more effective if we are careful to prime our communications with positive images and emotions.

Managers might choose words very carefully in performance reviews, recognizing that certain words will trigger a fight-or-flight response and shut down the higher cognitive functions in an employee's brain. And since you are hearing yourself using these words, be mindful of the effect of your own words on your brain. You may be telling yourself a situation is a "problem" when you are trying to present that it simply is a puzzle that you expect to solve.

On the other hand, there are times when the fight-or-flight response is exactly what is needed. In that case, the same principle applies. Don't wash over difficult issues with soft words, or you risk losing the impact you need to stimulate your audience to action.

Words and neuroplasticity

Neuroplasticity is the term used to describe how the brain continues to re-invent itself. Older, unused pathways fall away, and new ones, with repetition and focus, emerge. What we think about actually rewires our brains—for better or worse. We now know that our choice of words has a direct and immediate effect on our emotional response and makes our brains inclined to respond in specific ways. This is true whether we are reacting to spoken words delivered by someone else, or to the inner self-talk that we hear ourselves "saying" inside our heads.

Are we a race of singers?

An intriguing theory out of MIT suggests that human language may have evolved from imitating the songs of birds. As we learned how to express a wide range of emotions in song, we starting adding the first simple words to further clarify our meanings. We may be a race of singers. Could this be why American Idol seems to tap into something deeply tribal for so many of us?

What tune is your brain singing to you? What song do you want it to sing? How can you teach that song to others?

References

•Massachusetts Institute of Technology, Primitive Brain Is 'Smarter' Than We Think, MIT Study Shows, http://www.sciencedaily.com/releases/2005/03/050308134448.htm

•Julia Layton, How Fear Works, http://science.howstuffworks.com/life/inside-the-mind/emotions/fear2.htm

•Harvard School of Law, Negotiation and Neuroscience: Possible Lessons for Negotiation Instruction, http://www.pon.harvard.edu/research_projects/negotiation-pedagogy-program-on-negotiation/negotiation-and-neuroscience-possible-lessons-for-negotiation-instruction/

•Psychology Today, What is Oxytocin? https://www.psychologytoday.com/basics/oxytocin

•Shigeru Miyagawa, Robert C. Berwick and Kazuo Okanoya, The emergence of hierarchical structure in human language, http://journal.frontiersin.org/article/10.3389/fpsyg.2013.00071/abstract

•Peter Dizikes, How human language could have evolved from birdsong, http://newsoffice.mit.edu/2013/how-human-language-could-have-evolved-from-birdsong-0221

•Anneli Rufus, American Idol Is a Mind Game, https://www.psychologytoday.com/blog/stuck/200903/american-idol-is-mind-game

Music and the Mind

If you google the subject "music and the brain," your search will return approximately 587 million results. Many of these results will offer you a way to improve your brain power by listening to music—for a fee, of course.

While scientists will tell you that the so-called "Mozart Effect" has been greatly overstated, there is a large body of evidence that music works on our minds in powerful ways.

Music heals the mind

Moving to music has been shown to help patients with Parkinson's disease maintain greater control over their bodies, as well as improve their self-reported scores on the "Happiness Measure."

At least one study has shown music to be more effective than drugs for treating chronic anxiety. And music therapy can be successful in treating abused and traumatized children and adults with Post Traumatic Stress Disorder (PTSD).

These and other benefits of music on the mind are well-documented and have a basis in scientific research. It is even possible to become a board-certified music therapist and become a member of the American Music Therapy Association.

But what is music actually doing to our brains to create such a powerful effect on our behavior and our cognitive performance?

How music affects the brain

Listening to music triggers the brain's reward center, releasing dopamine, the chemical that makes us feel good. (Food and sex also stimulate the release of this chemical.) In fact, music's effect is so powerful that simply anticipating the experience gets the dopamine process started. This effect is heightened in the teenage brain, which appears to be even more susceptible to the power of music.

Music has also been associated with higher levels of immunoglobin A, an antibody linked to immunity. Music can also stimulate the production of serotonin, a chemical that helps us feel better.

Applications for human capital management

Corporate trainers have been using music for years, and the research has only recently caught up with what educators have intuitively known since Plato. But there are many other potential applications for music in the workplace that leverage the effect of music on the brain. Here are a few ideas:

- Group singing can build collaboration and team identity, so maybe there's a place for it in your next leadership retreat.
- Giving your employees music training can help them solve complex problems, or learn a new language. The introduction of music into employee development programs can increase the effectiveness of those programs and reduce time to mastery.
- Listening to certain types of music can increase worker productivity, while actually producing music can reduce stress and anxiety.
- Google employees have access to a recording studio, where they can find their inner Mozart.
- Should your organization get with the beat? Why not give it a try? At the very least, you will probably be able to move the happiness needle.

References

•J S Jenkins, MD FRCP, The Mozart effect, http://www.ncbi.nlm. nih.gov/pmc/articles/PMC1281386/

• Jessica Grahn, Music and the Brain: Jessica Grahn at TEDxWesternU, https://www.youtube.com/watch?v=fDfVsFxJXms

• Jim Morelli, MPH, Music Helps Movement, Mood in Parkinson's Patients, http://www.webmd.com/parkinsons-disease/news/20000620/music-helps-parkinsons-patients

• Time Magazine, Measure Your Happiness, http://content.time.com/time/interactive/0,31813,2028999,00.html

• Natalie van Rooy, Music therapy may reduce anxiety more than drugs before surgery: study, http://globalnews.ca/news/585987/music-therapy-may-reduce-anxiety-more-than-drugs-before-surgery-study/

• David L. Hussey, PhD, Music Therapy With Emotionally Disturbed Children, http://www.psychiatrictimes.com/articles/music-therapy-emotionally-disturbed-children

• Roberta Blake, Susan Bishop, The Bonny Method of Guided Imagery and Music (GIM) in Treatment of Post-Traumatic Stress Disorder (PTSD) with Adults in the Psychiatric Setting, http://www.hawaii.edu/hivandaids/TheBonnyMethodofGuidedImageryandMusicintheTxOfPTSDw AdultsPsychSetting.pdf

• American Music Therapy Assiation, http://www.musictherapy.org/

• V. Menona and D.J. Levitin, The rewards of music listening: Response and physiological connectivity of the mesolimbic system, file:///C:/Users/Margie/Downloads/The+rewards+of+music+listening.pdf

• Christopher Harris, Dopamine and the frontal lobes, https://www.youtube.com/watch?v=TI8-C9ZuLTA

• Valorie N Salimpoor, Mitchel Benovoy, Kevin Larcher, Alain Dagher & Robert J Zatorre, Anatomically distinct dopamine release during anticipation and experience of peak emotion to music, http://www.zlab.mcgill.ca/docs/salimpoor_2011_nn.pdf

•Farhad Manjoo, "This Is Your Brain on Music,"
http://www.salon.com/2006/09/05/levitin/
•Gunter Kreutz, Stephan Bongard, Sonja Rohrmann, Volker
Hodapp, Dorothee Grebe, Effects of Choir Singing or Listening
on Secretory Immunoglobulin A, Cortisol, and Emotional State,
http://link.springer.com/article/10.1007%2Fs10865-004-0006-9
•Ivan Hoffman, B.A., J.D., The Use Of Protected Materials In
Multimedia Corporate Training And Distance Education
Projects, http://www.ivanhoffman.com/protected2.html

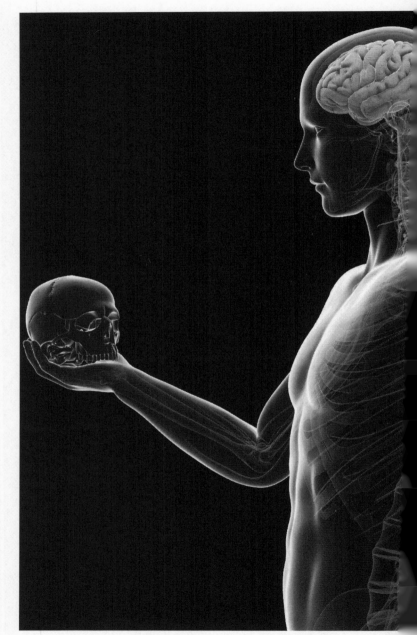

MIND/BODY CONNECTION

Give Learners the Gift of Brain Health

The discovery of brain plasticity has proven that you can help people change their brains almost immediately, by providing an environment to support learning. Since the brain learns better when it is healthy, adopting a healthier lifestyle can help learners develop brains that are more receptive to change and new ideas. Some of these lifestyle changes include:

- **Limit alcohol use.** Even a few drinks a week can reduce overall brain function and create areas of reduced brain function.
- **Maintain a healthy weight.** As your weight goes up, the physical size and function of your brain goes down.
- **Stop smoking.** Smoke inhalation blocks the carotid artery, restricting blood flow to the brain.
- **Manage high blood pressure.** Prolonged exposure to high blood pressure not only restricts blood flow to the brain, but increase the risk of dementia, heart attack and stroke.
- **Stop negative thoughts and cultivate positive ones.** When we formulate an idea, such as "I'll never be able to

lose weight," or "I'm good with people," a physical pattern, in the form of neural connections, is formed in the brain. Every time we go over this pattern by revisiting this thought, we make the behavior stronger.

- **Learn something new every day.** Brains with a high degree of new activity tend to stay that way. Brains that are slow to learn new things gradually lose some of their ability to change. Fortunately, this is a skill that can be learned.
- **Get at least 8 hours of sleep each night.** In our sleep-deprived world, the average adult is walking around in a brain-induced fog. The brain uses sleep to rebuild and reorganize. Sleep deprivation can result in lower brain performance and less ability to change.
- **Meditate.** Counter to previous beliefs, meditation has been shown to activate the cerebral cortex, which is the seat of conscious thought. A meditating brain is highly functioning brain.
- **Exercise.** Thirty minutes of physical exercise increases brain plasticity, making it more receptive to learning and change.

If you are a trainer, a mentor, a leader or educator, don't neglect the role of brain health in the process of learning. If you've been struggling with making some changes in your own life, take a look at your lifestyle and nutrition choices. You may need to make some changes there to get your brain ready for change.

References

•U.S. Department of Health & Human Services, Alcohol's Damaging Effects On the Brain, http://pubs.niaaa.nih.gov/publications/aa63/aa63.htm
•Daniel G. Amen, MD, Develop Brain Envy
To Avoid the Dinosaur Syndrome, http://www.

dorlandhealth.com/dorland-health-articles/
develop-brain-envy-to-avoid-the-dinosaur-syndrome
•Anonymous, Effects Of Smoking On The Brain, http://smoking.
ygoy.com/effects-of-smoking-on-the-brain/
•Harvard Health Center, Blood pressure and your
brain, http://www.health.harvard.edu/newsletter_article/
blood-pressure-and-your-brain
•James Clear, The Science of Positive Thinking: How Positive
Thoughts Build Your Skills, Boost Your Health, and Improve Your
Work, http://www.huffingtonpost.com/james-clear/positive-
thinking_b_3512202.html
•Psychology Today, How to Train Your Brain, https://www.
psychologytoday.com/articles/200604/how-train-your-brain
•Dr. Paul Nussbaum, The Importance of Sleep
for the Brain, http://www.rd.com/health/wellness/
the-importance-of-sleep-for-the-brain/
•Laura Schwecherl, Can Meditation Make You
Smarter? http://healthland.time.com/2012/08/10/
can-meditation-make-you-smarter/
•Justin Caba, Your Brain On Exercise: 30 Minutes Of
Physical Activity Makes Your Brain More 'Plastic,' http://www.
medicaldaily.com/your-brain-exercise-30-minutes-physical-
activity-makes-your-brain-more-plastic-308155

Healthy Body/Healthy Brain

In response to the growing costs of health care, many organizations have invested in wellness programs, hoping to prevent costly medical care for serious, partially preventable conditions such as diabetes, heart disease, and lung cancer. In fact, a recent study indicates that for every dollar spent on wellness programs, $4 of health care costs are avoided. If you are considering or managing a wellness plan, you might want to include brain health in your program. Here's why:

- By 2020, 25 percent of working Americans will be 55 or older.
- Roughly 40 percent of workers who retire today return to work in some fashion, often as contractors, consultants, or part-time employees.
- Older workers comprise the fastest-growing segment of the workforce.
- As we age, our brain is subject to cognitive decline, making it harder to concentrate, memorize, and perform other key cognitive functions that are critical to workplace performance.

If our aging workforce is to remain productive, employers need to encourage and support brain health.

Challenge: we don't know enough

While it is pretty clear that we can all benefit from taking care of our brains at any age, the problem is that we just know enough about how the brain ages—or how we can stop or slow down the effects of age. In fact, scientists are still struggling with how to separate the signs of "normal aging" with those of early dementia or serious illness.

Good nutrition and exercise help keep brains healthy

A common culprit of cognitive decline is a decrease in blood flow within the brain, caused by high cholesterol and high blood pressure. These blockages result in mini-strokes. Often undetected, these strokes damage the brain in small ways that have big cumulative effects. Just like any other organ in your body, the brain is affected by the overall health of the individual.

Existing employee health programs that concentrate on maintaining healthy weight, eating a diet high in fruits and vegetables, and regular exercise will also support healthy brains. The contrary is also true: Poor nutrition, smoking and lack of exercise contribute to general cognitive decline.

Use it or lose it

In this sense, the brain is like a muscle. People who participate in vigorous mental exercise later in life have a much greater chance of slowing or stopping cognitive decline. More than 29 percent of PhDs and engineers are working full-time after age 69, indicating that a more highly educated workforce may also be a more brain-healthy one.

The brain continues to produce new neurons, form new pathways, and learn new things throughout our lives. So the very fact that the aging workforce is, in fact, working is helping to keep those employees' brains healthy.

Aging brains have been shown to be more innovative and more empathetic than younger brains, making seniors highly valuable members of any project team.

Like a muscle, the brain gets stronger through repeated use and cross-training. Studies show that some brain activities are particularly useful in maintaining brain health, including:

- solving puzzles and math problems
- playing or composing music

Mind/Body Connection

- learning a language
- juggling

Employee wellness programs of the future

We talk a lot about the future in this book. Maybe that's because the field of neuroscience is pointing us to tantalizing applications that aren't quite realized yet, but are looming on the horizon. But maybe the future is actually within reach today, if we only exercise our brains to solve a few key puzzles. Should existing employee wellness programs address brain health? The answer to this question just might be a "no-brainer."

References

• Erten-Lyons D, Dodge HH, Woltjer R, Silbert LC, Howieson DB, Kramer P, Kaye JA., Neuropathologic basis of age-associated brain atrophy, http://www.alzforum.org/papers/neuropathologic-basis-age-associated-brain-atrophy

• William Klemm, Ph.D., What Happens to the Aging Brain, https://www.psychologytoday.com/blog/memory-medic/201211/what-happens-the-aging-brain

• Carl W. Cotman, Nicole C. Berchtold and Lori-Ann Christie, Exercise builds brain health: key roles of growth factor cascades and inflammation, https://softchalkcloud.com/lesson/files/H1a0Mp8O5SCTrQ/Exercise_and_the_Brain.pdf

• Daily Health Post, 6 Ways You're Causing Your Own Memory Loss, http://dailyhealthpost.com/6-ways-youre-causing-your-own-memory-loss/#ixzz3S1xyj02K

• Charles Q. Choi, Smart Strategy: Think of the Brain as a Muscle, http://www.livescience.com/4336-smart-strategy-brain-muscle.html

• William R. Klemm Ph.D., What Happens to the Aging Brain, https://www.psychologytoday.com/blog/memory-medic/201211/what-happens-the-aging-brain

•Amanda Enayati, The aging brain: Why getting older just might be awesome, http://www.cnn.com/2012/06/19/health/enayati-aging-brain-innovation

•Layla Merritt, How to Train Your Brain, https://www.psychologytoday.com/articles/200604/how-train-your-brain

Seeing is Believing

How we see

Here's what we know so far. Keep in mind that we are still learning about the brain and how it works, so more than likely if you re-read this post in a year, some of the information will have been updated based on new discoveries.

Light enters the eye and hits the retina in the back of the eye. The light stimulates specialized cells in the back of the brain (rods and cones) to emit a chemical called activated rhodopsin. This chemical produces electrical signals that are sent, one pixel at a time, to the brain. The raw data sent to the brain must be organized into a recognizable image, making meaning out of a steady stream of images that constantly are changing.

The brain is selective about what it sees

Studies show that different neurons seem to "like" different types of objects and tend to focus on specific types of images. These preferences may relate to survival, since paying attention to food or faces might be more important in the short run than looking at a pretty sunrise.

Understanding this selectivity has some interesting implications for the human capital professional. Scientists now are able to look at the patterns of firing neurons and identify the single object out of all of the objects in the visual field that is receiving the bulk of our attention at any given moment. This decoding of attention eventually may help us make training or reference materials more compelling and efficient. We may be able to train technicians to develop greater focus on those specific components that are most crucial to their work.

Eye wire: the game that maps the brain

When I started this blog I promised that we would have a chance to witness history together. How would you like to join me and thousands of others in actually making history? This innovative approach from MIT marries the power of crowdsourcing and the appeal of video games to create a map* of the retinal neurons in the brain. The game is easy to play and somewhat addictive. (Apparently, my brain was producing lots of oxytocin when I took the game for a spin.) The images that make up the maze come from the astounding work of the Big Brain Project, a 3D interactive image of the entire brain. Become a volunteer neuroexplorer! No experience necessary.

Is perception really reality?

When I was a new supervisor at a Fortune 100 company, my manager was constantly telling me that "perception is reality." This mantra seemed to be a justification for anyone to form any opinion of me that he chose, without any requirement for factual evidence. After all, what mattered most was how someone was "perceiving" me, and it was up to me to somehow manage that perception. But we now know that "reality" is a construct that is formed in each brain. It changes every fraction of a second as new information comes in. Our brains sift through the information and select or reject the information that fits our conscious and unconscious priorities. So it seems to me that a good leader, armed with this understanding of how the brain works, should hold people accountable for their perceptions and empower them to change those perceptions to be more productive.

What other uncharted lands will be mapped in the future?

Neuroscience is pointing the way towards a greater understanding of our inner world, and I hope with that understanding will come an increased ability to enhance our outer world—even though each of us sees it a little differently.

References

•Carl Bianco, MD, How Vision Works, http://health.howstuff works.com/mental-health/human-nature/perception/eye2.htm

•Wikipedia, Grandmother cells, http://en.wikipedia.org/wiki/Grandmother_cell

•James Di Carlo, MIT Museum Talkback 360 - Visualizing Science: All In Your Head, http://video.mit.edu/watch/mit-museum-talkback-360-visualizing-science-all-in-your-head-10622/

•Amy Robinson, Play a Game to Map the Brain, http://blog.eyewire.org/infographic/

•Abby Heiser, The 'Google Earth' of 3D Brain Maps is Here, http://www.thewire.com/technology/2013/06/google-earth-3d-brain-maps-here/66465/

•Tony D. Clark, Your Perception IS Your Reality, http://www.lifehack.org/articles/lifehack/your-perception-is-your-reality.html

•Evan Carmichael, Why We Should Hold People Accountable--And Why We Don't, http://www.evancarmichael.com/Leadership/5219/WHY-WE-SHOULD-HOLD-PEOPLE-ACCOUNTABLEAND-WHY-WE-DONT.html

Illusions

The predecessors of humans, the early mammals, developed an acute ability to see predators from many angles, which gave them an edge in the survival competition known as natural selection. However, that same survival skill can render us susceptible to wrong or falsely interpreted information—what scientists call visual illusions.

Shamans and magicians have used these illusions for years to create "magical" effects since the dawn of time, but we still don't really understand how most of them work. Let's take a look at one famous illusion: the Moon Illusion.

The moon illusion

For most people, the moon looks larger when it is near the horizon than it does when it is higher in our sky. However, the actual size of the image on the retina is always the same. So the fact that it looks "bigger" under certain circumstances is an illusion—and one that has been hard for science to fully explain.

For centuries, psychologists theorized that the illusion was a result of processing the distance cue of the horizon with the image. The explanation went something like this: when the moon is higher in our sky, we don't have anything to compare it to, and thus it appears smaller. This particular effect is called empty field myopia.

However, when neuroscientists showed various moon images to subjects undergoing Magnetic Resonance Imaging (MRI), they found that the images reported to be "larger" actually stimulated a larger section of the brain's visual cortex. In very simple terms, this revelation demonstrates that the brain isn't misinterpreting data by calculating relative distance, it is actually **perceiving** the moon as larger—even though the images are the same on the retina.

Mind/Body Connection

So, we could make the case that the moon illusion is not an illusion at all. The brain reports to our consciousness exactly what it "sees" when the moon is closer to the horizon. However, for some reason, the brain is making an error in processing the information.

This news still doesn't tell us why this is happening, but at least we have a clearer picture of how the brain processes this particular type of image to arrive at a false conclusion.

The moon illusion is certainly intriguing, but what does it have to do with human capital management? Well, it gives me an opportunity to debunk a truism I've heard many times in my career—and it drives me a little crazy.

Perception is reality—or is it?

Early in my career, I was promoted into my first management position. The popular mantra at the time was "perception is reality." I must have heard it five or six times a day (usually when someone was giving me "feedback" about how poorly I was doing in my new role).

I had a hard time getting my head around this statement because on the surface, "perception is reality" is clearly false. Most of us would say that there is a reality that can be measured and described by science (for example, the size of the image the moon consistently makes on the retina) and then there is human perception, which can be deceived and confounded by any number of factors (the position of the moon in the sky).

When I asked for an explanation, my peers and senior managers seemed to interpret this truism something like this: "Whatever anyone thinks about you feels true to them because that is how they perceive you. Therefore, you are being held accountable for other people's perception of you."

For an inexperienced and admittedly unskilled manager, this belief provided terrible advice. I spent way too much effort trying to change these "negative" perceptions of me when I should have been learning how to lead—accepting the fact that I might not be universally liked in the process.

Only years later was I able to see that one contributing factor to all that negative "perception" about me was probably the fact that I had been promoted to manage my former peers. I understand now why some of members of my team might have perceived me as arrogant and bossy, since they were looking through a lens that said they should have been promoted instead of me.

Of course, I probably did make a lot of mistakes. But telling me I had to accept all negative opinion about me as fact was certainly not helping.

What it really means

The phrase "perception is reality" appears to have originated with Lee Atwater, the political mastermind who orchestrated the first election of George W. Bush. He is credited with creating the negative campaign ad and the concept of "spin" in public relations. While these are significant accomplishments of a certain type in a particular field, I challenge any manager to make the case that spin and negative positioning truly have a place in managing and developing human beings.

The full quote, which is seldom used, is "Reality is irrelevant. Perception is reality." While it is true that people believe their perceptions to be reality, I like to think that we are all capable and willing to change our minds when presented with facts and evidence. Neuroplasticity teaches us that our brains are constantly remaking themselves, so there is hope for even the most ingrained prejudices to be removed in the face of new information.

Mind/Body Connection

If the moon illusion teaches us anything, it is that even our amazing brains can be mistaken at times. As leaders have a responsibility to acknowledge both perceptions **and** evidence in making decisions about the people in our organization.

As the car mirror says, "Things may be closer than they appear."

References

• Andrew Vanden Heuvel, The moon illusion,
https://www.youtube.com/watch?v=RXkYjL_7jME
• Skybrary, Empty Field Myopia,
http://www.skybrary.aero/index.php/Empty_Field_Myopia
• Web MD, Magnetic Resonance Imaging (MRI),
http://www.skybrary.aero/index.php/Empty_Field_Myopia
• Wikipedia, Spin,
http://en.wikipedia.org/wiki/Spin_(public_relations)
• Medicine.net, Definition of Neuroplasticity,
http://www.medicinenet.com/script/main/art.asp?articlekey=40362

Your Brain Needs a Vacation

After months of cold, windy, dreary winter, summer is finally upon us. Traditionally, this is the time to take a vacation, travel to new sites, take it easy, and break your regular routine.

Neuroscience tells us that this change of pace is extremely valuable. Your brain uses these new sensations to build new neural pathways, and the break from routine stimulates higher, more creative thought while it reduces stress. It is well-documented that overworked, over-tired employees are more accident-prone, have higher healthcare costs, and are less productive.

Yet, the average American worker left nine vacation days unused in 2012. Employees often state that they have too much work to take time off, or they fear employer retaliation for being a "slacker."

While this problem can occur in any country, it is particularly pronounced in the United States. The Center for Economic and Policy Research compared paid vacations in 21 prosperous nations and found that the U.S. ranked dead last in terms of the number of days provided and taken.

Don't be one of those statistics. Be a role model for your employees by embracing your vacation—and encourage your team and colleagues to do the same.

Vacation reading list

Another great summer tradition is taking the time to read a good book (or two.) There's something about reading a book that slows everything down. In a world where most of our information is delivered in bite-sized chunks, taking the time to let a story build, living with a book for days or weeks, builds a deeper, more experiential type of learning. Here are some books you can get right from the ATD store:

- *The Brain-Friendly Workplace* by Erika Garms. This book offers five practical strategies you can implement today to make your workplace more compatible with how our brains work.
- *Memory and Cognition in Learning by* Jonathan Halls. In keeping with the ATD *Infoline* tradition, this slim book gives you quick, targeted, practical information to help you apply the latest discoveries in neuroscience to the classroom or instructional design.

Want to delve deeper into the theory? Here are some books from my bookshelf that are sometimes used as college texts. They are a bit more challenging, but worth the effort. Pick and choose the chapters that interest you most.

- *Principles of Neural Science* by Eric Kanal et al.
- *Principles of Cognitive Neuroscience* by Dale Purves
- *Principles of Computational Neuroscience* David Sterratt et al.

Want to focus on the neuroscience of leadership? A great place to start is the Neuroleadership Institute, founded by David Rock. You'll find reading materials and educational opportunities on their site.

Through neuroscience, we've discovered that the brain is always changing. This state of constant transformation is called neural plasticity. But even our hard-working, ever-changing brain needs a vacation now and then. Research has discovered that people who go on a vacation to another location benefit from increased productivity and creativity upon their return. But vacation doesn't have to mean that you stop learning and growing. In fact, when you are otherwise unplugged from your usual routine, your brain will have time to revisit all the new information you've been pumping into your head for the past year. Cycling over new and older neural connections, your brain may find entirely new connections that did not exist before. I suggest that you take a little time on your next vacation to learn about neuroscience, not because you "have to," but because you "want to." The difference between reading for work and reading for pure pleasure is significant. A recent study shows that we often remember more of what we read for pleasure than what we are "assigned" to read for work or school.

Books:
- Neuroscience for Dummies, Frank Amthor
- Computational Cognitive Neuroscience, Michael Frank, Yuko Manakata, Thomas Hazy, Randall O'Reilly
- Introduction to the Math of Neural Networks, Jeff Heaton
- Brains: How they Seem to Work, Dale Purves

Websites and blogs:
- ATD Human Capital Blog: I am honored to be part of this vibrant community of scholar-practitioners.
- Sharp Brains: Tracking Health and Wellness Applications of Brain Science
- Brains: The Smithsonian page, "What does it mean to be human?"
- Center for Cognitive Neuroscience: Penn State's multidisciplinary community dedicated to understanding the neural bases of human thought.
- Genes to Cognition Online: Focuses on cognitive disorders, the cognitive process, and research.
- Hacking Knowledge: Ways to learn faster, better, cheaper.
- Psychology Today: Peer-reviewed articles on human behavior.
- Ted.com: Ideas worth spreading.
- Eyewire: Help us map the brain and have fun, too.
- ADD MY SITE

Mind/Body Connection

- ADD MOOCS
- ADD TV SHOWS/PBS

References

- Natalie Morera, Your Brain on Vacation,
http://www.clomedia.com/articles/your-brain-on-vacation

The Power of Play

I watch my middle-aged dogs go through the same ritual every day: They stare each other down, locking eyes, and freezing in mid-stride for several seconds. Then, as though an unseen signal has been transmitted, they leap away, tumbling over each other, and playtime begins.

If you've ever had a pet, you already know that domesticated animals like to play. In fact, there is pretty clear evidence that all animals play, not just the kittens and puppies on YouTube. Baby elephants slide down muddy hills; ravens snowboard on their bellies; herring gulls play catch in mid-air; even ants and inch worms have been caught at what appears to be playful activity.

Mystery of play

This behavior, so common across so many species, is something of a mystery to animal behaviorists. You see, from a biological point of view, animals select for behaviors that provide some kind of survival advantage.

So, if everyone is playing, there must something really special about it. We just haven't been able to prove what it is. And we are far from understanding the mechanism for play in the brain. What trigger makes my dogs agree that it's playtime?

For years, the assumption was that play was a chance to practice activities that would be helpful in adult life, such as fighting skills or tracking prey. There are two problems with this theory: 1) it has yet to be proven, and 2) it doesn't explain why adults still engage in play. One scientist tested this theory by tracking early play in meerkats and found no correlation between play and future survival.

This result has been repeated over and over again, as scientists have tried to prove the "value" of play. The very definition of "play" implies that it is an activity with no apparent value or purpose.

Window of neuroscience

Recently, neuroscience has opened a window on this mysterious behavior. Dr. Stuart Brown has been studying the nature of play using the tools of neuroscience. He traces play all the way back to the "big bang," when a massive explosion introduced random movement of atomic particles into the universe.

His work makes a compelling, evidence-based case that play begins at birth and enriches survival throughout our lives. He was able to place brain imaging devices on a mother and infant and capture the activity of the right cortex at the moment of mother-baby connection we call "baby talk." During this process, the cerebellum sends signals to the frontal cortex, stimulating language and cognitive functions.

Implications of play in human capital management

Engaging in play makes physical, positive changes in your brain. You become better at solving problems, improve empathy, recognize patterns, and handle stress. Cancer patients playing a game that lets them "shoot" cancer cells develop a more positive attitude towards their own illness and may improve survival rates.

Play is a natural and important brain activity that enhances performance. Maybe that's why places like Google and Zappos are considered great places to work.

The next time your pet or child is in a playful mood, join in! You'll be making new neural connections in the process.

References

•David Graeber, What's the Point if We Can't Have Fun? http://www.thebaffler.com/articles/whats-the-point-if-we-cant-have-fun#

•Anonymous, The Mystery of Play, https://www.patriciamcconnell.com/theotherendoftheleash/the-mystery-of-play

•Lynda Sharp, So You Think You Know Why Animals Play…, http://blogs.scientificamerican.com/guest-blog/2011/05/17/so-you-think-you-know-why-animals-play/

•Stuart Brown, THE NEUROSCIENCE OF PLAY: WHAT PLAY DOES FOR YOU AND YOUR BRAIN, AND WHAT HAPPENS TO YOU IF YOU DON'T PLAY, http://www.aspenideas.org/session/neuroscience-play-what-play-does-you-and-your-brain-and-what-happens-you-if-you-dont-play

•F.P. Hughes, Play, Creativity, and Problem Solving, http://www.education.com/reference/article/play-creativity-problem-solving/

•Emily Copeland, 5 Reasons Why Gaming Is An Effective Way to Teach Empathy (And Other Skills), http://startempathy.org/blog/2014/04/5-reasons-why-gaming-effective-way-teach-empathy-and-other-skills

•PRWeb, Video Games in the Brain: Study Shows How Gaming Impacts Brain Function to Inspire Healthy Behavior, http://www.prweb.com/releases/2012/3/prweb9293984.htm

•Venessa Miemis, Essential Skills for 21st Century Survival: Part I: Pattern Recognition, http://emergentbydesign.com/2010/04/05/essential-skills-for-21st-century-survival-part-i-pattern-recognition/

•Elizabeth Scott, M.S., Having Fun: Why It Provides Some of the Best Stress Relief, http://stress.about.com/od/funandgames/a/Having-Fun-Why-It-Provides-Some-Of-The-Best-Stress-Relief.htm

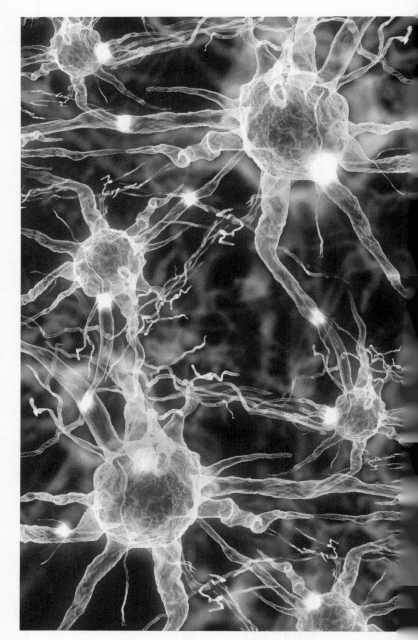

CONCLUSION

Writing about neuroscience these days is a bit like the advice the Queen of Hearts gave to Alice in Wonderland: We must run as fast as we can, just to stay in one place. However, the rapid pace of advancement in this field won't let us stay in one place, so we must accept the fact that any book on the subject is already at least partially out of date by the time it is published. I hope you've enjoyed this collection of essays on the application of neuroscience to learning, but I urge you to continue to seek out new information on the topic so that you can stay up-to-date.

I address these and other topics on a regular basis at learningtogo.com. You can also follow me on Twitter (margie. meacham@twitter.com.)

Remember that your brain is always seeking new information and eliminating information that hasn't been used in a while, so if you found this book helpful:

- Use the suggestions as a starting point for your own projects.
- Share this book with others and tell them what you learned from reading it.
- Visit learningtogo.com often to share information with other learning professionals.

Thanks!